Barbara Kerr's

Taste

of Health

◆

Gourmet Vegetarian Recipes

Especially Created for People with
Crohn's & Colitis or Lactose Intolerance

Much of the material in this book previously appeared on the Three Angels Broadcasting Network programs "3ABN Presents" and "Food for Thought." In case of discrepancies between instructions given on the programs and instructions in the book, please follow the book.

This book was produced by Taste of Health Ministries P.O. Box 38, Gaston, SC 29053 *www.tasteofhealth.net* (803) 936-1714

Printed and bound in the United States of America by Color House Graphics, Grand Rapids, Mich.

ISBN 1-930984-00-6

Dedicated in loving memory of Leonard Warren, a man whose quiet example shone brightly to all who knew him.

1937–2000

BARBARA KERR'S

TASTE
OF HEALTH

◆

Gourmet Vegetarian Recipes
Especially Created for People with
Crohn's & Colitis or Lactose Intolerance

PHOTOGRAPHY BY PAT CRAWFORD

FOOD STYLING BY CHRIS VALANNE,
FRAN WOOSLEY AND BARBARA KERR

DESIGN BY JUDY ANDERSON

EDITING BY JAN ASHER DOLPH

TASTE OF HEALTH MINISTRIES
GASTON, S.C.

TABLE OF CONTENTS

Foreword: Optimal Nutrition, Vital for People with Digestive Diseases

Excellent nutrition in a healthy, tasteful and colorful presentation contributes to a positive outlook on life—so important in healing and health maintenance.

Inflammatory bowel disease (Crohn's and ulcerative colitis) can lead to the development of nutritional deficiencies for several reasons:

• An intestine affected by disease or surgical resection may have a decreased ability to assimilate nutrients.
• Increased losses of nutrients in diarrheal stools also contribute to vitamin and mineral deficiencies.
• Poor nutritional intake is common, because of poor appetite, fear of diarrhea or abdominal pain, and occasionally associated psychological depression.
• Deficiencies in potassium, magnesium, zinc, iron, calcium, vitamin B_{12} and folate are not uncommon.
• Deficiencies in protein, essential fatty acids, and vitamins A, D, E and K can also occur.

Reasons to Eat Right

Optimal nutrition can improve your health in three important ways:

1. A healthful diet can correct and prevent nutritional deficiencies.
2. Eating right goes beyond correcting deficiencies towards enhancing and optimizing health, function and longevity. Optimal nutrition rich in vitamins, minerals, essential fatty acids and protein can restore nutrient losses and enhance the body's ability to heal itself. Certain nutrients, such as omega-3 fatty acids, have healing properties in Crohn's disease. Certain soluble fibers, such as pectin in bananas, slow diarrhea and enhance colonic intestinal health. Fruits and vegetables are rich sources of antioxidants (including vitamins A, C, E, zinc, selenium, and various carotenoids such as carotene and lycopene) and other substances that promote optimal health, function and longevity, and even have anticancer properties.
3. Nutritious, well-presented and tasteful foods can enhance psychological well-being. Excellent nutrition in a healthy, tasteful and colorful presentation contributes to a positive outlook on life—so important in healing and health maintenance.

Beyond the Ordinary

Barbara Kerr has the wonderful ability to blend healthful nutrition into a colorful, tasteful presentation that goes beyond the ordinary towards the extraordinary in health and nutrition.

C. Berkelhammer, MD, FACG

Charles Berkelhammer, M.D., FRCP (C), FACG
Associate Professor of Medicine and
Gastroenterology, University of Illinois

INTRODUCTION:
A MINISTER OF HEALTHY CUISINE

Dear Friends,

There are youth ministers, ministers of music, ministers of the Word, but have you ever heard of a minister of healthy cuisine? That is the title that is so befitting to Barbara Kerr. Healthy cooking is not just a hobby with her, it's a ministry!

Barbara almost lost her life to a disease that stemmed from the typical American diet. For years she struggled with an abnormal reaction and sensitivity to food, and food was something she needed to survive. Then, after many tears, prayers, doctors, prescriptions and heartaches, the answer came. A diet straight from nature, loaded with life-giving enzymes, and a simple healthy lifestyle finally brought healing to her body.

There are no words to adequately describe how you feel when you've looked death in the face. I know, because I've been there. But one thing is for sure—you're never the same again. Your perspectives are forever changed.

Barbara now LIVES to tell her story and share with others how lifestyle and diet changes can make all the difference in the world! Her kitchen is the sanctuary where she prays for heavenly recipes that will make a healthier, happier world...recipes that will offer answers to someone who might be desperately searching for them like she once did. The recipes in this cookbook not only contain ingredients from the garden and your local health food store, they also contain a heaping helping of a heart that really cares...and that is the heart of Barbara Kerr. ENJOY!

Best wishes,

Linda Shelton

Linda Shelton
Vice President
Three Angels Broadcasting Network

Lifestyle and diet changes can make all the difference in the world!

Barbara and Linda celebrate a successful taping of the Mother's Day show with cups of peach punch (page 34).

SHOPPING WITH BARBARA

It's so much easier to make a new recipe if you have all the needed ingredients on hand.

Growing up eating meat made becoming a vegetarian a difficult and even painful process for me. I loved the taste of chicken, beef and fish. Most of my recipes incorporated meat in some way or another. I loved fancy desserts and baking tasty treats for others, something that still gives me great joy. When I could no longer consume sugar and meat without immediately getting sick or experiencing painful stomach cramps, I had to find an alternative. I began to look for healthier recipes and try them at home. I was greatly disappointed in the taste and texture most of the time.

One Thanksgiving several years ago, I had had enough. Out of desperation and sheer redheadedness, I began making healthful pumpkin pies (without using eggs or evaporated milk) in an attempt to satisfy my taste buds. By the fifth pie I had succeeded—victory was mine. I had even fooled my father-in-law. That very pie recipe is included in this book.

As I began looking for more and more alternatives to those familiar but unhealthful ingredients, I began coming across words I was unfamiliar with—sucanat, whole-wheat pastry flour, brown rice syrup, liquid aminos. It's a bit intimidating to shop for a recipe ingredient when you have no clue what it looks like. So it is my wish, in this shopping section, to explain some of the more unusual ingredients in my recipes.

Make a list to take to your health food store, grab one of the store clerks and have them shop with you. Trust me, it will save you a lot of time. It's so much easier to make a new recipe if you have all the needed ingredients on hand.

In this list and throughout my cookbook where I call for specific name brands, it's because I have looked for products that have:
• Labels with ingredients I can pronounce!
• No dairy or other animal products.
• No or low amounts of hydrogenated fat.
• Natural sweeteners; no refined sugar.
• No monosodium glutamate (MSG).
• Great taste.

A warning: Please be aware of a food coloring additive called *carmine* and/or *cochineal extract*. It is extracted from the bodies of a South American female scale insect. It is being used to color yogurts, fruit juices, pill coverings, makeup and more. Write or call these companies, asking them to remove the offending ingredients.

Following is a list of things I recommend adding to your pantry. You can find these items at nearly any health food store, and if you don't have a health food store nearby, don't despair. In my resources section (page 128), you will find information on health food by mail from Country Life Natural Foods.

MILK SUBSTITUTES

Silk soy milk by White Wave—my number one favorite soy milk. Found in red and blue cartons only in the refrigerated section.

West Soy unsweetened soy milk—has a light consistency, good for soups.

Almond milk by Pacific Foods of Oregon, Inc. (Naturally Almond)—found in one-quart cartons on the shelf.

TOFU (HIGH IN PROTEIN)

Silken tofu—a soybean product with a silky smooth texture. Great for pies and puddings. Mori-Nu's boxed silken tofu is excellent.

Nasoya water-packed tofu—comes in 16-ounce tubs in extra firm, firm and soft consistencies. Has a firm, grainy texture. Good crumbled as a burger or egg texture replacement.

MAYONNAISE SUBSTITUTE

Vegenaise by Follow Your Heart—my favorite mayonnaise replacement. Found only in the refrigerated section.

NATURAL SWEETENERS

Sucanat by Wholesome Foods—organic evaporated sugar cane juice with black strap molasses added to it. Replaces brown and white sugar one-for-one.

Pure maple syrup—inexpensive if purchased at large membership stores.

Brown rice syrup by Lundberg—mildly sweet. Can replace corn syrup in some recipes.

Milled cane sugar by Florida Crystals—use as white sugar one-for-one in recipes that need to be light in color, such as cheesecake.

Sorghum—a rich-tasting molasses.

Welch's 100 percent frozen fruit juices—I love these as sweeteners. All-natural ingredients.

CAROB CHIPS

Vegan Sunspire carob chips—my favorite brand of carob chips (I never use generic chips).

Chatfield's dairy-free carob chips—grain-sweetened and also very tasty. These chips have a slightly sticky consistency when melted.

SEASONING

Liquid aminos by Bragg—an unfermented soy sauce replacement.

Bill's Best Chik Nish seasoning by Nutri-Line Foods—a chicken boullion replacement. This is low in sodium, so you may have to adjust salt.

GRAINS

Quinoa—a small round grain containing all of the essential amino acids. Must be rinsed prior to use.

Whole-wheat pastry flour—whole-wheat flour that has been ground out of soft wheat berries to a finer consistency than regular whole-wheat flour. Great in pastries.

Honey graham crackers by Hain—made from wholesome ingredients and no hydrogenated fats.

GELATIN

Emes Kosher-Jel—contains no animal products.

Super Fruits by Hain—a Jell-O replacement with no animal products. Several fruit flavors.

BEVERAGES

Water—I use only pure, distilled water for drinking and in my recipes. (I do cook pasta and wash vegetables in tap water.)

Rice Dream—a nondairy brown rice beverage with a light, sweet taste.

Roma—a noncaffeinated coffee substitute.

Hokan Lite coconut milk—found in super stores such as Super Wal-Mart. Contains only a fraction of the fat of regular coconut milks (35 calories per quarter cup).

OTHER PRODUCTS

Baking powder—Rumford's makes an aluminum-free baking powder.

Better Than Ice Creme by Better Than Milk—a powdered lactose-free, cholesterol-free, caseinate-free ice-cream replacement. Comes in 21-ounce cans that make 3 quarts of vanilla ice cream. Tastes great.

All-fruit jams—use generic or Pollaner or make your own. These jams are made from fruit and fruit juices. Sugar and corn syrup have not been added. Great for sandwiches.

Natural peanut butter—my favorite brand is Roddenbury's. It's inexpensive and fresh. Look for jars without a lot of oil floating at the top; they're fresher. If the peanut butter is soft, I pour off some oil to reduce the fat calories. Your kids don't need sandwiches loaded with sugar and hydrogenated fat; look for labels that read *peanuts* and *salt* only.

TRY IT!

If you're really interested in changing your or your family's diets and want to be successful, please try these steps:

• Choose one meal per week (could be breakfast, lunch or dinner); it should be a meal when every family member is present.

• Make one new recipe experiment. This could be a healthful drink, entree, side dish or dessert.

• At the meal's conclusion, everyone votes. It's either a thumbs up—a keeper, or a thumbs down—you ditch it.

The neat part is, at the end of the year, even if you like only half the recipes you tried, you'll end up with at least 26 new ones to replace your less heart-healthy dishes.

May God richly bless you in your attempts to live a healthier lifestyle.

I hope this shopping list will help get you started on a successful path to a new way of eating. May God richly bless you in your attempts to live a healthier lifestyle.

ESSENTIAL NUTRIENTS

PROTEIN: THE RIGHT AMOUNT, THE RIGHT KIND

*P*rotein is an essential nutrient for growth and maintenance of the body's living tissues.

In the case of protein, as with other nutrients, more is not necessarily better. Too much protein for an extended period of time can damage the kidneys and cause other health problems. An excessive intake of protein can also displace the intake of other important nutrients, including some B vitamins and vitamin C.

The average healthy adult needs no more than ½ gram of protein per pound of ideal body weight per day (Example: A 150-pound individual would need no more than 75 grams of protein per day). Children, pregnant or lactating women, overweight adults, athletes, underweight people, and those who are ill or injured have different protein needs.

About half of a person's protein requirement should be from "high-quality" or "complete" protein sources. High-quality proteins contain all of the amino acids, or building blocks, of protein that are required to sustain human life. Examples of animal sources of high-quality protein include meat, poultry, fish, milk, cheese and eggs. Healthier non-animal sources include soy protein, meat substitutes and combinations of other legumes with grains, nuts and seeds.

Examples of combination protein sources include peanut butter on whole-wheat bread, red beans with brown rice, lentils with brown rice, and pinto beans with corn.

The protein content of different foods tends to vary, with meat, poultry and fish providing approximately 7 grams of protein per cooked ounce. One cup of milk yields about 8 grams of protein, while soy milks vary widely in their protein content. Barbara Kerr's favorite soy milk, Silk by White Wave, yields 7 grams of protein per 8-ounce cup. One egg, two egg whites or ⅓ cup egg substitute yields about 7 grams protein, while ½ cup legumes contains about 7 grams, and ½ cup grain about 3 grams. Meat substitutes vary in their protein content, so check the labels.

The volume of a plant-based protein diet is larger, promoting greater satiety and ample fiber that is not found in animal foods. A person would need to eat 1½ cups of beans to equal the protein found in 3 ounces of meat (which is the size of a deck of cards).

Current diet plans that promote quick weight loss via high protein and low carbohydrate intake are unhealthy and potentially dangerous. A more healthful approach to permanent weight loss is an intake that includes plant-based protein; large amounts of vegetables; moderate amounts of whole grains and fruits; small amounts of nuts, seeds and added fats; and avoidance of processed grains and added sugars.

FAT: MAKING HEALTHFUL CHOICES

The average healthy adult requires an approximate minimum of 1 to 2 teaspoons (or 5 to 10 grams) of fat per day in the form of Omega-3 and Omega-6 fatty acids. These specialized types of fat are essential for maintaining human life.

Humans cannot manufacture Omega-3 and Omega-6 fats, but these fats can be abundantly found in soybean fat, canola oil, flaxseeds and walnuts. The most healthful fats are those eaten in their most natural form, such as walnuts or flaxseeds themselves, not the oils extracted from them.

This wonderful cookbook provides many healthful, high-quality protein meat alternatives that will not only be great for your body, but will also tempt the taste buds and give new meaning to the words "Soul Food"!

If oils are to be used in cooking, however, it is highly advisable to purchase those that are "cold-pressed" or "expeller-pressed." This means that the oil has not been subjected to high temperatures and/or chemicals, which could change the molecular structure and render the oil harmful to the human body. Processed oils may potentially cause certain types of cancer. Hydrogenated fats and animal fats are considered to be contributors to coronary artery disease. Cold-pressed oils should be refrigerated. Oil sprayers/misters are available at gourmet cooking shops and can be used with cold-pressed oils to coat pots and pans for cooking and baking.

The maximum amount of fat recommended for adults is 20 to 40 grams per day for women, and 30 to 60 grams per day for men. Note that 1 tablespoon of most types of oil or 1 ounce of most types of nuts yields about 14 grams of fat.

THE BENEFITS OF SOY

The list of the many benefits of soy foods continues to grow. Soy foods have been shown to provide high-quality protein and fiber, to play a major role in cancer and heart disease prevention, to ease the discomforts of menopause and premenstrual syndrome (PMS), to help protect bone mass in the aging population and to help stabilize blood glucose.

Soy products include many vegetarian meat substitutes, soy milk, soy cheese, tofu, tempeh, miso, protein powders and snack bars. Take care to avoid excessive processed sugars and fats in some soy products. The most healthful diet plans should include 2 to 3 servings of soy foods each day to maximize the many benefits of soy.

TIPS FOR WEIGHT MAINTENANCE

1. Eat a wide variety of unprocessed foods.
2. Eat slowly and only until comfortably full (NOT "Thanksgiving-Day" full!).
3. Avoid large meals or snacking in the evenings (this is when you need calories the least).
4. Avoid processed fats, processed grains and processed sugars.
5. Fill up on healthful foods.
6. Remember the Law of Diminishing Returns: that is, you receive 99 percent of the pleasure of a food within the first few bites.

SUGGESTED ONE-DAY MENU
USING BARBARA KERR'S *TASTE OF HEALTH*:

Breakfast: Hot nutty quinoa with almonds and freshly ground flaxseed topped with diced kiwi and whole blueberries; Silk soy milk.

Lunch: Roasted gazpacho with grilled pimento cheese sandwiches; Barb's Waldorf salad; fresh fruit; carrot juice.

Supper: Grilled tofu and vegetables with brown rice and unforgettable baked beans; fresh fruit juice.

Snack: Homemade granola or whole-grain cereal with soy milk.

This wonderful cookbook provides many healthful, high-quality protein meat alternatives that will not only be great for your body, but will also tempt the taste buds and give new meaning to the words "Soul Food"!

In good health,

Roberta Jupp, R.D., CDE

Roberta Jupp
Registered Dietitian
Certified Diabetes Educator

Let's Have a Party!
New Year's Eve or
Super Bowl Sunday Menu

Best Pimento Cheese Sauce

Western Potato Rounds

Cinnamon Chips

Key West Fruit Salsa

Cancun Salsa

Seven-Layer Dip

Carob Muddy Buddies

Radish Mouse Garnish

Pictured, clockwise from bottom left: Western Potato Rounds, Cinnamon Chips with Key West Fruit Salsa, Carob Muddy Buddies, Cancun Salsa

Best Pimento
CHEESE SAUCE

Laughter is the sun that drives winter from the human face.
—Victor Hugo

Serve this as a dip, or bake it into your favorite cheese recipe (for example, macaroni and cheese or lasagna).

1 cup water
¾ cup raw cashew pieces
3 tablespoons nutritional yeast flakes
1¼ teaspoons sea salt
2 teaspoons onion powder
¼ teaspoon garlic powder
½ cup pimentos (don't drain)
2 tablespoons lemon juice
1 teaspoon dill weed

1. Blend half of the water with cashews until silky smooth.

2. Add remaining ingredients and blend again. Now the mixture is ready to be baked into a cheese sauce recipe.

Or to serve as a dip, put the sauce into a pan, and stir constantly over medium heat until thickened.

Serves 5

Nutrients per serving: Calories 143, Protein 5g, Carbohydrate 11g, Fat 9g, Cholesterol 0mg, Saturated Fat 2g, Sodium 547mg, Dietary Fiber 2g

Western
POTATO ROUNDS

4 large baking potatoes (about 2½ pounds), washed
Canola oil spray
Salt
⅛ cup seedless blackberry all-fruit jam
½ cup Classico sun-dried tomato sauce
1 tablespoon chopped cilantro
1 can (15 ounces) black beans, drained and rinsed
1 medium to large tomato, diced small
2 cups shredded mozzarella cheese substitute

1. Cut potatoes into ¼-inch slices with a knife or garnishing tool. (A garnisher makes a wavy pattern on the potato.)

2. Spray both sides of potato rounds with canola oil and salt lightly.

3. Bake in a single layer on a cookie sheet or baking stone at 450 degrees F for 20 minutes, or until the edges begin to brown. You do not need to flip them.

4. In a 1-quart saucepan, melt jam over medium heat.

5. Add tomato sauce, cilantro, beans and tomato.

6. When potatoes are tender, put 1 scant tablespoon of sauce mixture in the center of each potato slice. Top with a sprinkle of cheese and pop back into the oven for 5 minutes, or until cheese is melted. Serve warm or cold.

Serves 10

Nutrients per serving: Calories 219, Protein 10g, Carbohydrate 38g, Fat 3.5g, Cholesterol 0mg, Saturated Fat <1g, Sodium 350mg, Dietary Fiber 4g

Cinnamon
CHIPS

¼ cup pure maple syrup
1 teaspoon cinnamon
6 whole-wheat, low-fat Garden of Eatin tortillas

1. Mix syrup and cinnamon together in a small bowl.

2. Using a pastry brush, brush both sides of each tortilla with the syrup mixture.

3. Using a pizza cutter, cut each tortilla into 8 slices. Arrange in a single layer on a baking sheet.

4. Bake at 400 degrees F for 14 minutes or until crisp and lightly browned. (The top side of each chip will be glossy-looking.)

5. Cool chips on a cooling rack before serving with your fruit salsa (recipe at right).

One batch makes 48 chips.

Serving: 6 chips

Nutrients per serving: Calories 178, Protein 4g, Carbohydrate 32g, Fat 3g, Cholesterol 0mg, Saturated Fat 0g, Sodium 184mg, Dietary Fiber 2g

Key West
FRUIT SALSA

1 cup fresh or frozen raspberries
2 kiwifruit, peeled, sliced and quartered
1 large Granny Smith apple, peeled, cored and diced small
1 cup fresh or frozen blueberries
1 can (15 ounces) peaches in natural juice, drained and chopped small
1 teaspoon lime zest
2 tablespoons lime juice
2 tablespoons honey

1. Lightly toss together prepared fruit.

2. Whisk zest, juice and honey together in a small bowl and pour over fruit.

3. Mix well and serve with cinnamon chips (recipe at left).

Serves 10

Nutrients per serving: Calories 55, Protein 1g, Carbohydrate 14g, Fat <1g, Cholesterol 0mg, Saturated Fat 0g, Sodium 3mg, Dietary Fiber 2g

What oxygen is to the lungs, such is hope to the meaning of life.
—Emil Brunner

Cancun
SALSA

3 cups tomatoes, diced small
¾ to 1 cup sweet onion, diced very small
½ teaspoon salt, or to taste
⅛ cup fresh cilantro, chopped
⅓ to ½ cup lime juice

Mix all and serve with your favorite healthful chips.

Serves 8

Nutrients per serving: Calories 27, Protein 1g, Carbohydrate 6g, Fat <1g, Cholesterol 0mg, Saturated Fat 0g, Sodium 141mg, Dietary Fiber 1g

MY SALSA INSPIRATION

Several years ago while visiting Cancun, I fell in love with their salsa. It was never spicy; instead the prominent flavors were cilantro and lime.

Seven-Layer
DIP

1 can (16 ounces) Bearitos, vegetarian refried black beans, traditional
1 large ripe avocado, peeled and mashed
½ teaspoon garlic salt
¼ cup Tofutti Sour Supreme, Better than Sour Cream
¼ cup Vegenaise
1 package (1.25 ounces) Ortega taco seasoning mix
2 large ripe tomatoes, finely chopped
½ cup sliced black olives (measurement is after slicing)
1 to 1½ cups pimento cheese sauce (page 16), cooked
½ cup chopped green onions, green part only

1. Spread beans evenly on the bottom of a 9 x 9-inch baking pan.

2. Mash avocado with garlic salt and spread evenly over beans.

3. Whisk together in a small bowl the sour supreme, Vegenaise and the taco seasoning packet until smooth. Spread over avocado layer.

4. Evenly sprinkle a thick layer of tomatoes, and then the black olives.

5. Spread prepared pimento cheese sauce over the olives. Use as much of the sauce as you like.

6. Top that by sprinkling on the green onions. You can serve this dip as is, but I like to warm it thoroughly in the oven at 325 degrees F for 20 minutes. Don't actually bake it to bubbling because it will ruin the avocado. Enjoy!

Serves 8

Nutrients per serving: Calories 224, Protein 6g, Carbohydrate 19g, Fat 15g, Cholesterol 0mg, Saturated Fat 2.5g, Sodium 1004mg, Dietary Fiber 4g

Carob
MUDDY BUDDIES

Wondering what to do with your old turkey roaster? It's perfect for mixing up a batch of muddy buddies! (A Dutch oven is too deep and narrow, and you would end up crushing a lot of the cereal.)

- 2 cups carob chips, unsweetened or grain-sweetened
- 1 cup all-natural peanut butter
- ¼ cup canola oil
- 9 cups (17-ounce box) shredded wheat, bite-sized, not sweetened
- ½ cup pure maple syrup
- ½ cup carob powder
- ½ cup powdered barley malt sweetener

1. Melt chips, peanut butter and oil over low heat, stirring often.

2. Put shredded wheat in a large bowl.

3. Pour peanut butter mixture over the cereal and mix well, coating evenly.

4. Pour maple syrup over mixture and toss well to coat.

5. In a separate bowl, sift together carob powder and barley malt. Use a spoon to smash any lumps if necessary. Mix your cereal one more time to make sure there isn't any syrup lying in the bottom of the bowl, and add the powdered mixture to the shredded wheat. Toss quickly, mixing well. The cereal will separate and become slightly dry-looking.

Serves 24

Nutrients per serving: Calories 230, Protein 6g, Carbohydrate 38g, Fat 11g, Cholesterol 0mg, Saturated Fat 4g, Sodium 61mg, Dietary Fiber 4g

Radish
MOUSE GARNISH

Your guests will be surprised when they see mice peeking up at them from your "cheese" party trays!

- 3 radishes
  - 1 large (body)
  - 1 medium (head)
  - 1 medium to small (ears)
- 3 round toothpicks
- 2 cloves for eyes

1. Select radishes that still have their "tails."

2. Wash radishes; cut off any leaves.

3. Select the "head" radish and cut off the root, leaving a small white spot for the mouse's nose.

4. Attach the body to the head with a toothpick.

5. Press the 2 cloves into the face for eyes.

6. Cut each remaining toothpick into 3 equal pieces. Put 3 "whiskers" on each side of the mouse's nose using cut toothpicks.

7. Cut a ⅜-inch v-shaped slit behind each eye to hold the ears. Using the third and smallest radish, cut 2 fairly thin slices and push each slice into the wedges you made for the ears.

Train up a child in the way he should go; and when he is old, he will not depart from it.
—Proverbs 22:6

Hors d'Oeuvres

Chik Nish Sandwich Spread

Tofu-Olive Ranch and Tex-Mex Spread

Mini Veggie Quiches

Thai Peanut Dipping Sauce

Carrot-Stuffed Cucumbers

Black Olive Penguins

Orange-Sugared Pecans

Pictured, bottom front row from left to right: Chik Nish Sandwich Spread in filo cups, Carrot-Stuffed Cucumber, Tofu-Olive Tex-Mex Spread, Black Olive Penguins, Chik Nish Sandwich Spread-filled cherry tomatoes, Mini Veggie Quiches
Epergne double-decker square by Mosaicwares

Chik Nish
SANDWICH SPREAD

The gift of friendship is a wondrous thing, with the joy and happiness good friends bring.
—Unknown

Great stuffed in lightly salted cherry tomatoes or on Triscuits, toast or in sandwiches. This recipe is a slight adaptation of a sandwich spread in Bill's Best Cookbook. *(See my resources section, page 128.) I've found that this recipe does not taste good with any substitutions of the seasoning or the mayonnaise.*

1 pound extra-firm or firm water-packed tofu, drained and mashed
5 teaspoons Bill's Best Chik Nish seasoning
½ can (about ¾ cup) black olives, diced small
Vegenaise to taste, about ½ cup

1. Mash tofu and add rest of ingredients.

2. Stir to blend. You want this to be the consistency of egg salad. Add more Vegenaise if it is too dry.

Serves 12

Nutrients per serving: Calories 103, Protein 5g, Carbohydrate 3g, Fat 8g, Cholesterol 0mg, Saturated Fat <1g, Sodium 269mg, Dietary Fiber <1g

Tofu-Olive
RANCH & TEX-MEX SPREAD

1 can black pitted olives, chopped fine
½ cup green olives, chopped fine
½ cup green onion, chopped, green part only
¼ cup red pepper, diced fine
¼ cup yellow pepper, diced fine
1 cup extra-firm water-packed tofu, drained and mashed

RANCH SPREAD:
2 tablespoons Vegenaise
¼ teaspoon dill weed

TEX-MEX SPREAD:
3 tablespoons favorite spaghetti sauce
2 teaspoons jalapeño, diced very fine, no seeds

1. Mix together olives, green onion, diced peppers and tofu in a large bowl.

2. Divide mixture in half, about 1½ cups in each bowl.

3. Add ranch spread ingredients to one bowl and Tex-Mex ingredients to another.

4. Chill 2 hours before serving. Spread on Triscuits to serve, or stuff cherry tomatoes with filling.

Serves 6

Nutrients per serving (Ranch): Calories 83, Protein 3g, Carbohydrate 4g, Fat 7g, Cholesterol 0mg, Saturated Fat <1g, Sodium 455mg, Dietary Fiber .5g

Nutrients per serving (Tex-Mex): Calories 64, Protein 3g, Carbohydrate 4g, Fat 5g, Cholesterol 0mg, Saturated Fat <1g, Sodium 494mg, Dietary Fiber .5g

Mini VEGGIE QUICHES

Your friends won't believe this recipe doesn't have cheese in it! You can also use the filling for lasagna. Just layer between noodles, and add an extra cup or two of sauce around the edges and on top before baking. This recipe is perfect for a crowd.

1 large onion, sliced thin
2 to 3 tablespoons olive oil
1 medium zucchini, sliced thin
1 medium to large yellow summer squash, sliced thin
1½ teaspoons salt
1 can (7 ounces) mushrooms, stems and pieces, drained
1 can black pitted olives, diced small
1 cup favorite spaghetti sauce
½ pound extra-firm water-packed tofu, drained and mashed
1 tablespoon Bill's Best Chik Nish seasoning
3 tablespoons Vegenaise
1 box (16 ounces) filo dough, thawed for 5 hours

1. Sauté onion in oil until it begins browning.

2. Add zucchini, summer squash and salt.

3. Cook until tender, about 5 minutes.

4. Stir in mushrooms, olives and sauce.

5. In a separate bowl mash tofu and stir in seasoning and Vegenaise. Add to tomato mixture. Remove from heat.

To assemble:

1. To work with filo dough, you will need plastic wrap, vegetable oil spray, a large cutting board and a tea towel. You will need to work quickly when the dough is uncovered to keep it from drying out.

2. Remove the dough from the protective wrap and lay it on your countertop. Cover it immediately with 2 pieces of plastic wrap. Top that with a tea towel that has been dampened with water and wrung out. Now you are ready to begin.

3. Pull back the towel and wrap, remove one sheet of filo dough, and place it on a large cutting board. Re-cover main dough.

4. Spray first sheet with vegetable oil, making sure to spray edges. This does not have to be heavily sprayed.

5. Pull out the second sheet of dough and place it directly on top of first and spray it with oil. Repeat this until you have 4 pieces of dough on top of each other.

6. Using a sharp knife, cut dough into 1½- to 2-inch squares. Place each square into an oiled mini-muffin tin and press down with a dough press or your fingers.

7. Fill each cup with a teaspoon of the vegetable filling and bake at 350 degrees F for 20 to 25 minutes or until edge of dough is browning and crisp. Serve warm or at room temperature. Makes 75 to 100 mini quiches.

Serves 75

Nutrients per serving: Calories 24, Protein 1g, Carbohydrate 2g, Fat 2g, Cholesterol 0mg, Saturated Fat 0g, Sodium 134mg, Dietary Fiber <1g

To know someone here or there with whom you can feel there is understanding in spite of distances or thoughts unexpressed— that can make this life a garden.
—Goethe

Thai Peanut
DIPPING SAUCE

Serve this sauce cold with your favorite veggies or spring rolls.

1 cup Hokan Lite coconut milk
½ cup water
½ cup all-natural creamy peanut butter
1 tablespoon lemon juice, fresh
1 tablespoon sucanat
1 teaspoon ground coriander
⅛ teaspoon cayenne
½ teaspoon powdered vegetable broth
   and seasoning
1 medium to large clove garlic, pressed
⅛ cup minced green onion, white part

1. Combine all ingredients in a medium saucepan over medium heat. Bring to a low boil for 5 minutes.

2. Cool completely.

Makes 12 one-ounce servings

Nutrients per serving: Calories 81, Protein 3g, Carbohydrate 4g, Fat 6g, Cholesterol 0mg, Saturated Fat 2g, Sodium 62mg, Dietary Fiber 1g

Carrot-Stuffed
CUCUMBERS

These beautiful carrot-stuffed cucumber slices can be topped with dip or eaten plain. If assembled according to directions, the slices can be made up to 24 hours ahead of serving time and carefully stored in ice water.

1 fat-at-both-ends straight carrot
1 large straight cucumber
Apple corer
Vegetable peeler
Lemon zester/scorer
Garnisher

1. Starting at one end of the cucumber, alternate running the scoring edge from top to bottom with the zesting edge. This will create a thick-thin-thick-thin pattern of cuts all the way around the cucumber.

2. Next, use the garnisher (makes a wavy cut) and slice off ½ inch from each end of the cucumber.

3. Holding the cucumber straight up and down, center the apple corer over the top and press it gently down the center of the cucumber as far as it will go. Carefully pull it back out.

4. Turn the cucumber over, center the corer on that end, and begin pushing down until the cuts connect and the center can easily be pushed out.

5. Using your vegetable peeler, peel the carrot until it is slightly larger than the diameter of the apple corer. (If you peel too much carrot off, it will fall out of the center of your cucumber once it is sliced. And if you try to push the carrot in and it's too fat, you could break open the cucumber.)

6. When the carrot is the right size, gently push it through the cucumber.

7. Using the garnisher, cut ¼-inch slices.

Serves 8

Nutrients per serving: Calories 9, Protein <1g, Carbohydrate 2g, Fat 0g, Cholesterol 0mg, Saturated Fat 0g, Sodium 4mg, Dietary Fiber 1g

Black Olive
PENGUINS

Your guests—especially the kids—will love these.

FILLING:
½ **pound extra-firm water-packed tofu, drained**
1 **tablespoon Bill's Best Chik Nish seasoning**
¼ **cup Vegenaise**
2 **teaspoons Emes plain, unflavored gelatin**

1 **can small black olives, drained**
1 **can jumbo black olives, drained**
1 **medium to large carrot, peeled and sliced into thin rounds**
Frill toothpicks

1. Blend tofu, seasoning, Vegenaise and gelatin in food processor until smooth.

2. Fill Easy Accent Decorator, or a decorating bag, and attach the writing tip.

3. Chill for 1 hour.

To assemble:

1. Set out a bowl of each: small olives, jumbo olives and carrot rounds. Keep toothpicks close by.

2. Begin with a carrot round. They are the feet. Using a paring knife, cut a small "v" out of the carrot. The small "v" is the beak.

3. Take a small olive and make a sideways cut in the center just big enough to insert the wide end of the beak. You have completed the head.

4. Now take a jumbo olive and slice from top to bottom on one side only.

5. Insert the writing tip of the decorator into the "pit hole" end of the jumbo olive and begin filling. Fill until the filling begins to expand the "chest." You want it to open about ⅛ inch. Run your knife over the filling to make it smooth and even with the olive edges.

6. Take a frill toothpick and run it through the "x" end of the small olive, through the "x" end of the large filled olive and into the carrot round. Make sure the small "v" cut in the carrot is in line with the front of the penguin. Serve immediately.

Serves 60

Nutrients per serving: Calories 19, Protein 1g, Carbohydrate 1g, Fat 1.5g, Cholesterol 0mg, Saturated Fat 0g, Sodium 92mg, Dietary Fiber <1g

Orange-
SUGARED PECANS

1½ **cups sucanat**
½ **cup fresh orange juice**
1½ **teaspoons grated orange rind (fresh gives a strong flavor, dried is mild)**
¼ **teaspoon salt**
4 **cups pecan or walnut halves or a mixture of both**

1. In a saucepan bring sucanat, juice, rind and salt to 250 degrees F.

2. Remove from heat; stir in nuts to coat well.

3. Turn out onto waxed paper and separate. Break apart when hard. Nuts will sugar overnight.

Makes about 30 one-ounce servings

Nutrients per serving: Calories 146, Protein 1g, Carbohydrate 10g, Fat 10g, Cholesterol 0mg, Saturated Fat <1g, Sodium 66mg, Dietary Fiber 1g

If you have knowledge, let others light their candles by it.
—Unknown

Valentine's Menu

Curried Tomato, Potato & Garlic Soup

Great Garlic Bread

Wild-For-You Salad with Roasted Heart-Shaped Beets

Barb's Raspberry House Dressing

Raspberry Sweetheart Pie with Crunchy Graham Cracker Crust

Dark Cherry Tart

Tropical Frost #1

Pictured, clockwise from bottom left: Curried Tomato, Potato, & Garlic Soup; Great Garlic Bread; Dark Cherry Tart; Raspberry House Dressing; Wild-For-You Salad with Roasted Heart-Shaped Beets

Curried Tomato,
POTATO & GARLIC SOUP

*Many waters
cannot quench love;
rivers cannot wash it away.
—Song of Solomon 8:7*

2 pounds baking potatoes (about 5), cut
   into 1-inch pieces
2¼ pounds plum tomatoes, quartered
1 head garlic
3 to 4 tablespoons olive oil
1 teaspoon salt, or to taste
2 teaspoons dried or fresh thyme
1½ teaspoons curry powder
3½ cups distilled water
3½ teaspoons McKay's chicken-style
   seasoning
½ cup almond milk
Juice of one lemon

1. Scrub potatoes and remove any bad spots.
Peeling is optional; I don't.

2. Cut into large cubes and put in one half of a
10 x 14-inch pan.

3. Wash and quarter tomatoes; cut in large pieces.
Put tomatoes in the other half of your pan. If
necessary, use two pans.

4. Put the head of garlic in the middle, and
drizzle all with olive oil. Evenly sprinkle the salt
and thyme over the vegetables.

5. Roast for 20 minutes at 400 degrees F.

6. Remove from oven and sprinkle curry powder
evenly over tomatoes and potatoes. Toss gently
to mix curry in, keeping your vegetables separated.

7. Return to oven and roast an additional 20 to
30 minutes, or until soft. Set aside for garlic bread
(recipe at right) ½ cup of the roasted tomatoes
and remaining garlic.

8. In batches if necessary, put potatoes, tomatoes
and 5 cloves of roasted garlic through your food
processor and grind into a somewhat chunky
paste. I like mine a little lumpy.

9. Put processed vegetables in a 6-quart Dutch
oven and add water, McKay's seasoning, lemon
juice and almond milk.

10. Heat through; no need to boil. Garnish the
top of each bowl of soup with a fresh sprig of
thyme. Serve with garlic bread.

Serves 10

*Nutrients per serving: Calories 153, Protein 3g,
Carbohydrate 26g, Fat 5g, Cholesterol 0mg,
Saturated Fat <1g, Sodium 393mg, Dietary Fiber 3g*

Great
GARLIC BREAD

*Make Curried Tomato, Potato & Garlic Soup, and
you'll have all the extra roasted tomatoes and garlic
you'll need for this recipe. Enjoy!*

5 or 6 slices of your favorite whole-wheat
   bread
Roasted garlic, skins removed
½ cup roasted tomatoes, skins removed
Salt
Thyme leaves

1. Lightly toast bread.

2. With a fork, mash garlic and tomatoes together.
Salt to taste, and spread on bread.

3. Lightly sprinkle thyme leaves on each slice.

Serves 6

*Nutrients per serving: Calories 65, Protein 3g,
Carbohydrate 12g, Fat 1g, Cholesterol 0mg,
Saturated Fat <1g, Sodium 250mg, Dietary Fiber 3g*

Wild~For~You
SALAD WITH ROASTED HEART-SHAPED BEETS

1 bag Dole spring mix salad—
   baby lettuce, endive, mustard greens—
   any wild salad greens will work
2 cups radicchio lettuce (small red heads,
   look a bit like cabbage)
2 to 3 medium large beets
1 to 2 tablespoons olive oil

1. Freshen the lettuce with cold water and drain well.

2. Cut the radicchio into small strips, and toss together with the wild greens.

3. Wash the beets and cut the tops off. Do not peel before baking.

4. Place each beet in a double layer of foil and drizzle each with a teaspoon or two of olive oil. Wrap the foil up to seal the beet inside.

5. Roast beets in a 400 degrees F oven for about 1 hour, or until soft.

6. Remove and rinse with cold water until cool enough to handle.

7. Using a paring knife, gently peel the beets. The skin should pull off easily.

8. Using a garnisher, or knife, slice the beets into ¼-inch slices. I have a set of assorted plastic heart-shaped cookie cutters and, finding the right size for each beet slice, I cut out one heart shape from each slice.

9. You can put the salad into individual bowls and decorate the tops with 3 or 4 heart-shaped beets, or use one big salad bowl and scatter the hearts on top. Serve the salad with raspberry dressing (recipe at right).

Serves 5

Nutrients per serving: Calories 63, Protein 2g, Carbohydrate 5g, Fat 4g, Cholesterol 0mg, Saturated Fat <1g, Sodium 23mg, Dietary Fiber 2g

Barb's Raspberry
HOUSE DRESSING

This dressing is a beautiful deep burgundy color and won't separate for several hours.

⅓ cup canola oil
⅓ cup distilled water
⅓ cup 100 percent juice, frozen grape juice concentrate
⅔ cup fresh or frozen raspberries, packed into cup
1 tablespoon apple cider vinegar or lemon juice
¼ teaspoon salt (omit if using lemon juice)

Place all ingredients into a blender and blend on high. Discard any leftovers after 7 days.

Makes 14 two-tablespoon servings

Nutrients per serving: Calories 54, Protein 0g, Carbohydrate 4g, Fat 4g, Cholesterol 0mg, Saturated Fat 0g, Sodium 32mg, Dietary Fiber <1g

A wife of noble character is her husband's crown.
—Proverbs 12:4

Raspberry
SWEETHEART PIE

I like to make this pie in an 8-inch heart-shaped pie plate.

1 bag (12 ounces) frozen raspberries (reserve 1 cup for garnish)
2 boxes (12.3 ounces each) of Mori Nu Lite firm, silken tofu
2 packages (3.85 ounces each) vanilla Mori Nu Mates, low-fat pudding mix
Graham cracker crust (recipe at left)
Mint leaves

1. Bring the raspberries to room temperature, keeping the reserved raspberries frozen.

2. Blend thawed raspberries with 2 boxes of tofu till smooth. You will need to be patient and stop your blender several times to scrape down the sides. When the tofu mixture is smooth, add the pudding mix. This will take about 5 minutes of blending time before it becomes smooth and the sugars dissolve.

3. If your blender holds a small capacity, consider blending the recipe in 2 batches, and mix the two batches together well.

4. Pour into cooled graham cracker crust, and garnish the edges of your pie with the frozen raspberries and a few mint leaves. Refrigerate for two hours before serving. This dessert needs to be served cold.

Serves 10

Nutrients per serving: Calories 137, Protein 5g, Carbohydrate 19g, Fat 5g, Cholesterol 0mg, Saturated Fat 0g, Sodium 93mg, Dietary Fiber 2g

Crunchy
GRAHAM CRACKER CRUST

This recipe is also listed with my carob fudge pie (page 78).

8 large squares honey-flavored, all-natural graham crackers, crushed into crumbs
3 tablespoons pure maple syrup
2 tablespoons canola oil

Do everything in LOVE.
—1 Corinthians 16:14

1. Mix well.

2. Pat into 9-inch crust and bake at 350 degrees F for 12 minutes, or until it begins to brown on edges.

Serves 8

Nutrients per serving: Calories 90, Protein 1g, Carbohydrate 11g, Fat 5g, Cholesterol 0mg, Saturated Fat 0g, Sodium 59mg, Dietary Fiber <1g

Dark
CHERRY TART

Your sweetheart is bound to love this delectable delight!

CRUST:
⅓ cup sucanat
1 cup pecan meal
1 cup quick oats
¾ cup whole-wheat pastry flour
½ cup canola oil

1. Mix together to form crumbs. Set aside ½ cup for topping.

2. Pat the rest of the crust into the bottom of an 11-inch tart pan, or a 10-inch quiche pan. (If using a 10-inch pan, you may not be able to fit in all of the dark cherries.)

FILLING:
1 can (12 ounces) Welch's white grape raspberry 100 percent juice, frozen concentrate
3 tablespoons Minute tapioca
2 bags (12 ounces) frozen dark sweet cherries (Kroger's grocery is one place to find these)

1. In a saucepan, combine juice concentrate with tapioca and bring to a boil.

2. Simmer on low for 2 or 3 minutes.

3. Keep cherries frozen until ready to use. Arrange a single layer of cherries over crust, filling in all the gaps.

4. Pour juice mixture over cherries in a circular pattern trying to distribute liquids evenly.

5. Sprinkle remaining crust mixture on top and bake at 400 degrees F for 35 to 40 minutes, or until bubbly and the crust has slightly browned.

Serves 14

Nutrients per serving: Calories 323, Protein 3g, Carbohydrate 42g, Fat 17g, Cholesterol 0mg, Saturated Fat 1g, Sodium 23mg, Dietary Fiber 3g

Tropical
FROST #1

½ cup Port Arthur Lite coconut juice
¼ cup fresh lime juice
1 ripe banana, broken into 3 pieces
1 tablespoon shredded, unsweetened coconut
1 tablespoon honey
6 ice cubes

1. Blend everything except ice cubes on high until smooth.

2. Add ice cubes and blend again. Makes a nice frosty tropical drink.

Variations:

Can be topped with additional shredded coconut. You may also use a frozen banana for a more "ice cream"-like drink, but it takes much longer to blend.

Serves 4

Nutrients per serving: Calories 70, Protein 1g, Carbohydrate 15g, Fat 1.5g, Cholesterol 0mg, Saturated Fat 1g, Sodium 3mg, Dietary Fiber <1g

The first duty of love is to listen.
—Paul Tillich

Easter Menu

Korean Spring Stir-Fry

Ginger Dressing

Oriental Salad

Raspberry Foamy

Key Lime–Coconut Parfait

Leek Flower Garnish

Pictured, clockwise from bottom center: Korean Spring Stir-Fry, Leek Flower Garnish, Oriental Salad with Ginger Dressing on the side, Key Lime–Coconut Parfait, Raspberry Foamy
Three-tier cake stand by Mosaicwares

Korean Spring
STIR-FRY

This dish is very colorful and pleasing to the eyes, nose and mouth! This recipe can easily be halved. Mung bean noodles have no taste when they are cooked; we give them the flavor. You will need to go to an Asian market to find them. They are a wonderful noodle to work with. Dark sesame oil may also be purchased at an Asian market.

Water enough to boil noodles in 6-quart Dutch oven
1½ teaspoon salt
12 ounces mung bean oriental noodles, large or small
¼ cup plus 2 tablespoons sesame oil
2 stalks celery, sliced into ½-inch diagonals
1 large onion, sliced into strips
5 cups napa cabbage, sliced thin
½ cup liquid aminos, divided
1 red pepper, sliced thin and cut in half
1 yellow pepper, sliced thin and cut in half
2 cups shredded carrots
Salt

God raised Him from the dead, freeing Him from the agony of death, because it was impossible for death to keep its hold on Him.
—Acts 2:24

1. Bring salted water to a boil. Add noodles and boil for 6 to 7 minutes, or until noodles become clear. Pour noodles into colander and rinse with cold water for several minutes. It is important to remove the starch by rinsing so your noodles won't stick together. Set aside.

2. Heat ¼ cup of the sesame oil in a deep 12-inch skillet or wok, and sauté celery and onion until slightly tender and celery turns bright green.

3. Add cabbage and sauté till reduced by half. Add ¼ cup liquid aminos and toss.

4. Add rinsed noodles and gently combine with the celery, onion and cabbage.

5. Pour the 2 tablespoons of sesame oil and liquid aminos over all.

6. Continue to heat through while combining the noodles and veggies.

7. As soon as the vegetables are mixed in and the noodles are hot, remove from heat and carefully add red and yellow pepper slices and shredded carrots. Salt to taste. You do not want to cook the peppers and carrots, just warm them through.

Serves 8

Nutrients per serving: Calories 293, Protein 4g, Carbohydrate 58g, Fat 10g, Cholesterol 0mg, Saturated Fat 1g, Sodium 1363mg, Dietary Fiber 3g

Ginger Dressing

Excellent served hot or cold!

1 teaspoon fresh minced garlic
⅜ cup (¼ + ⅛) lemon juice
¼ cup liquid aminos
¼ cup honey
1 tablespoon grated ginger
2 teaspoons mustard powder
¼ cup sesame oil
2 teaspoon carrot puree (chop or process to mush)
2 tablespoons celery puree

Combine all in a medium saucepan. Heat without boiling, and serve.

Makes 10 two-tablespoon servings

Nutrients per serving: Calories 87, Protein 1g, Carbohydrate 13g, Fat 6g, Cholesterol 0mg, Saturated Fat <0g, Sodium 267mg, Dietary Fiber 0g

Oriental Salad

½ head iceberg lettuce, cut up
½ head romaine lettuce, cut up
2 cups napa cabbage, sliced thin
1 cup purple cabbage, sliced thin
1 medium tomato, diced small
½ red, yellow or orange pepper, cut into thin strips
1 carrot, shredded

Toss together in a large bowl and serve with ginger dressing (recipe at left).

Serves 12

Nutrients per serving: Calories 15, Protein 1g, Carbohydrate 3g, Fat 0g, Cholesterol 0mg, Saturated Fat 0g, Sodium 10mg, Dietary Fiber 1g

Let me live that I may praise you, and may your laws sustain me.
—Psalm 119:175

FLAVORS OF KOREA

Korean food has always intrigued me. The dishes are loaded with color and unusual flavors. The tastes of sesame and ginger are my favorites.

Mung bean noodles are transparent and stretchy. They not only taste great, but are also fun to eat!

Raspberry *Foamy*

1 can (12 ounces) frozen white grape
   raspberry 100 percent juice concentrate
3 cans water
2 cups frozen raspberries

1. Combine concentrate and water in a pitcher and stir.

2. Pour about one third of the juice mixture into a blender, add the raspberries, and blend until smooth.

3. Add to the other juice mixture and stir to combine all. Serve immediately.

Serves 16

Nutrients per serving: Calories 67, Protein 0g, Carbohydrate 17g, Fat 0g, Cholesterol 0mg, Saturated Fat 0g, Sodium 2mg, Dietary Fiber <1g

Look to your health; and if you have it, praise God, and value it next to a good conscience; for health is the second blessing that we mortals are capable of; a blessing that money cannot buy.
—Izaak Walton

CHOOSING YOUR TOFU

When a recipe calls for tofu, make sure you use the right type. Silken should be used in pies, puddings, dressings and sauces—anything smooth and creamy. Water-packed tofu should be used in recipes that need texture. It can be crumbled into a "scrambled egg" or "burger" texture. The two types of tofu are rarely interchangeable.

Key Lime– *Coconut Parfait*

If you're a real lime-lover, like me, add some lime zest!

1 cup lime juice
2 teaspoons coconut extract
2 boxes (12.3 ounces each) Mori Nu Lite
   firm, silken tofu
2 packages (3.85 ounces each) Mori Nu
   Mates, vanilla low-fat pudding mix
½ teaspoon lime zest (optional)
Shredded, unsweetened, toasted coconut
Lime slices

1. Blend lime juice, coconut extract and tofu until smooth and creamy.

2. Add pudding mix and, if desired, lime zest. Continue blending until smooth. Be patient. You will need to stop your blender several times to stir down the mixture. The sugars will dissolve and it will become completely smooth.

3. Pour into elegant wine or parfait glasses to serve. Garnish the top of each glass with coconut and a slice of lime.

Serves 6

Nutrients per serving: Calories 97, Protein 7g, Carbohydrate 14g, Fat 2g, Cholesterol 0mg, Saturated Fat 0g, Sodium 77mg, Dietary Fiber 0g

Leek
FLOWER GARNISH

This garnish can be made up a day ahead and stored in ice water until needed.

1 large leek, roots still attached
1 medium carrot

TOOLS:
Paring knife
Tomato corer
Toothpick
Bowl filled with ice water

1. You will be working with the root end of the leek. Carefully cut the roots off without actually detaching the part that holds everything together.

2. Go up about 4 to 5 inches from root end and cut off the rest.

3. Pinching the root end with one hand, begin making cuts ¼ inch apart that begin ½ inch from the root end and run all the way to the top of the leek. Cut only halfway through the leek. This will allow you to go completely around without losing control of your flower.

4. Open up the leek and push back some of the petals. Put it in ice water while you make the center.

5. Using the tomato corer, press firmly into the carrot, rotating and scooping at the same time. This forms a perfect little carrot ball.

6. Remove the leek flower from the water and shake gently. Open up carefully.

7. Break a toothpick in half, and stick one end into the carrot and the other end into the center of the leek. You can now place your flower back into the water, which will curl the petals, or you can place your garnish on your table ready for dinner.

MAKING GARNISHES
When making garnishes, always work with vegetables and fruits that are room temperature. They will be more flexible and less likely to break.

For I know the plans I have for you, declares the Lord, plans to prosper you and not to harm you, plans to give you hope and a future.
—Jeremiah 29:11

FOR MOTHER WITH LOVE

ASPARAGUS-FILLED CREPES WITH A DILL CAPER SAUCE

VEGGIE-STUFFED ZUCCHINI ROUNDS OR MUSHROOM CAPS

BABY RED POTATOES

LEMON GRANITA WITH HONEYDEW MELON RIBBONS

APPLE TARTLETS

PERFECTLY PEACH PUNCH

Pictured, clockwise from bottom left: Lemon Granita with
Honeydew Melon Ribbons, Apple Tartlet, Asparagus-Filled
Crepes with a Dill Caper Sauce, Baby Red Potatoes,
Veggie-Stuffed Zucchini Rounds, Perfectly Peach Punch
Rectangular tray by Mosaicwares

Asparagus-Filled
CREPES WITH
A DILL CAPER SAUCE

A mother is not a person to lean on, but a person to make leaning unnecessary.
—Dorothy Canfield Fisher

When shopping for asparagus, look for slender, bright green, crisp spears. Eating asparagus is good for your heart!

2 bunches fresh asparagus spears (about 1½ to 2 pounds)
1 large cucumber, for garnish

CREPES:
¾ cup water
½ cup firm water-packed tofu, not silken
½ cup brown rice flour
2 teaspoons honey
½ teaspoon salt
1 teaspoon onion powder
¾ teaspoon dill weed

DILL CAPER SAUCE:
1 cup Vegenaise, original flavor
1 teaspoon dill weed
1 tablespoon capers, drained (optional)

1. Wash and snap off bottom 1½ inches of each spear.

2. Steam to crisp tender 4 to 5 minutes. Asparagus will be bright green and crisp, not soft.

3. Using the scoring edge of a garnishing tool, cut long strips of peel from the cucumber. The strips will be used to gently tie the crepes around the asparagus later.

4. In a blender, process the crepe batter until smooth.

5. Cook in a large nonstick skillet in ⅛ cup portions until golden brown, making the crepes slightly oval-shaped.

6. In a medium-sized mixing bowl stir together sauce ingredients. Refrigerate until ready to assemble.

To assemble:

1. Warm plates in oven for serving.

2. Place 3 or 4 asparagus spears in the center of a crepe. Gently roll up.

3. Take a cucumber strip and, with the dark green side facing in, carefully tie, making sure not to pull too hard.

4. Top with a dollop of dill caper sauce and serve immediately.

Serves 15

Nutrients per serving: Calories 141, Protein 3g, Carbohydrate 9g, Fat 10g, Cholesterol 0mg, Saturated Fat 1g, Sodium 161mg, Dietary Fiber 1g

Veggie-Stuffed ZUCCHINI ROUNDS

4 to 5 medium 1½- to 2-inch diameter
    zucchini
½ cup zucchini, finely chopped

FILLING:
½ cup broccoli, finely chopped
¼ cup carrot, finely chopped
1 tablespoon onion, finely chopped, or
    dried minced onion
1 cup Pepperidge Farm cubed herb
    seasoned stuffing (crushed, about
    ½ cup)
½ teaspoon salt
1 tablespoon Bill's Best Chik Nish
    seasoning
⅛ cup canola oil

1. Wash and remove ends from zucchini.

2. Using a ruler, measure and cut zucchini in
1-inch rounds. I slice mine using a garnisher,
which gives them a wavy look.

3. Using a tomato corer (looks like a small melon
baller, only with teeth), scoop out zucchini pulp
from each round leaving ¼ inch on the sides and
bottom. You are forming small cups to hold your
vegetable filling.

4. Chop broccoli, carrot and onion.

5. Process stuffing cubes to a fine crumb texture
and add to chopped vegetable mixture.

6. Stir in salt and seasoning. Mixture should be
moist, not wet.

7. Using a 1-tablespoon scoop, fill each
zucchini round, mounding it just slightly in
the center. Press the mixture gently down.

8. Bake in an oiled pan at 400 degrees F for
35 minutes or until lightly brown on top.

Makes about 25 rounds; serves 25

*Nutrients per serving: Calories 22, Protein 1g,
Carbohydrate 3g, Fat 1g, Cholesterol 0mg,
Saturated Fat 0g, Sodium 90mg, Dietary Fiber 1g*

Veggie-Stuffed MUSHROOM CAPS

20 to 23 large mushrooms (1½- to 2-inch
    diameter), about 1 pound
½ cup mushroom stems, chopped fine

FILLING:
Recipe at left

1. Cut a thin slice from the stem end of each
mushroom and discard.

2. Using a tomato corer, remove stems and make
a small hollow in each mushroom cap, leaving
¼ inch on sides and bottom.

3. Prepare filling as in steps 4, 5 and 6 at left.
Add chopped mushroom stems.

4. Fill each mushroom cap, mounding up the
filling in the middle. Press it down slightly.

5. Bake in an oiled pan at 400 degrees F for
20 minutes, or until lightly brown and mushrooms
are beginning to shrivel slightly. Good served
warm or room temperature.

Serves 25

*Nutrients per serving: Calories 21, Protein 1g,
Carbohydrate 2g, Fat 1g, Cholesterol 0mg,
Saturated Fat 0g, Sodium 89mg, Dietary Fiber <1g*

*Honor thy father and
thy mother: that thy
days may be long upon
the land which the
Lord thy God
giveth thee.
—Exodus 20:12*

Baby RED POTATOES

2 pounds baby red potatoes, quartered
1 tablespoon canola oil
4 tablespoons water, divided
⅛ cup fresh parsley, slightly packed into cup
1 envelope Campbell's onion soup mix
¼ teaspoon salt
½ teaspoon imitation butter flavor

1. Scrub and cut potatoes into ½ inch pieces. Put into a large bowl.

2. Coat with oil, 1 tablespoon water, parsley and soup mix.

3. Put potatoes into a lightly oiled 10-inch quiche pan.

4. Add 2 tablespoons water to the dish without pouring it over the potatoes.

5. Cover with foil and bake 40 minutes at 400 degrees F. Uncover and bake 15 more minutes.

6. When done, sprinkle with salt, 1 tablespoon water and butter flavor. Mix well and serve hot.

Serves 12

Nutrients per serving: Calories 102, Protein 2g, Carbohydrate 21g, Fat 1g, Cholesterol 0mg, Saturated Fat 0g, Sodium 342mg, Dietary Fiber 2g

Lemon Granita
WITH HONEYDEW MELON RIBBONS

A granita is a cross between a frozen drink and a flavored ice, very popular in Italy. The consistency should be slushy, not solid. It can be made at home with the help of a food processor.

¾ cup Welch's 100 percent white grape frozen concentrate
1¾ cups water
Grated rind of one lemon, scrubbed before grating
½ cup fresh lemon juice (4 to 6 lemons)
1 honeydew melon, for garnish

1. Stir together in medium bowl juice concentrate, water, lemon rind and lemon juice.

2. Stir again just before pouring mixture into two ice cube trays. Freeze.

3. When ready to serve, process 8 to 9 cubes at a time in a food processor. Allow to sit for five minutes while you prepare the melon ribbons.

4. Cut the melon in half and remove seeds.

5. Using a vegetable peeler, peel off the rind in a 3 or 4-inch area. Continue to peel same area, making long ribbons from the melon.

6. Place about ½ inch of melon ribbons in the bottom of each serving dish and top with 3 one-tablespoon scoops of granita.

7. Store unused cubes in a freezer bag until ready to serve. Four cubes make 1 serving.

Serves 6

Nutrients per serving: Calories 106, Protein <1g, Carbohydrate 28g, Fat 0g, Cholesterol 0mg, Saturated Fat 0g, Sodium 8mg, Dietary Fiber <1g

Apple Tartlets

4 cups Granny Smith apples, peeled,
cored, sliced and chopped (about
4 large)
1 cup apple juice, unsweetened
1 teaspoon ground cinnamon
2 teaspoons pure vanilla extract
½ cup sucanat
⅛ cup pure maple syrup
2 tablespoons cornstarch
1 tablespoon apple juice or water
2 boxes (17.3 ounces each) Pepperidge
Farm puff pastry sheets

1. In a medium saucepan, bring the apples and
1 cup juice to a low boil and simmer covered for
5 minutes.

2. Add cinnamon, vanilla, sucanat and maple
syrup.

3. In a separate cup dissolve the cornstarch and
liquid. Add to above boiling mixture and stir
until thickened. Remove from heat.

4. Thaw and carefully remove pastry sheets from
first box. Keep them refrigerated until 15 minutes
before use, or they become too sticky to work with.

5. Lightly flour a large cutting board or cutting
surface and a cookie sheet or baking stone. Open
first sheet of pastry onto floured surface.

6. Spread with half of the apple filling to ½ inch
from edges. Top with remaining pastry sheet.

7. Using a 2½-inch ravioli press, cut out 9 squares.
I use a paring knife to cut around the edges of
the press to help make the cuts all the way
through the dough.

8. Gently remove the squares and place them on
your floured baking sheet at least 1 inch apart. It
is not necessary for the tartlets to be sealed.

9. Bake at 400 degrees F for 20 minutes or until
nicely puffed and brown.

10. Repeat above procedure with remaining
ingredients and be sure to cook up your scraps,
too. They are delicious!

Serves 18

*Nutrients per serving: Calories 132, Protein 1g,
Carbohydrate 19g, Fat 5g, Cholesterol 0mg,
Saturated Fat 0g, Sodium 65mg, Dietary Fiber <1g*

Perfectly Peach Punch

*This fresh, delicious punch requires some advance
preparation, but it's worth it!*

8 cups unsweetened orange juice; fresh
is best
6 cans (15 ounces each) peach slices
(8 cups when drained)

1. Drain and freeze peaches in 6 separate freezer
bags 2 to 3 days before party.

2. On the day of the party juice oranges, or mix
concentrate with water.

3. When ready to serve, blend 2 cups juice and
2 cups peach slices until smooth. Repeat until
ingredients are used.

4. Pour into a punch bowl.

ICE RING:
1 cup frozen raspberries, sprinkled
around ice ring
2 to 3 cups punch mixture (1 cup orange
juice plus 1 cup blended peaches)

Make ahead and freeze to float in punch when
ready to serve. Garnish with a few ivy sprigs.

Serves 32

*Nutrients per serving: Calories 46, Protein <1g,
Carbohydrate 11g, Fat 0g, Cholesterol 0mg,
Saturated Fat 0g, Sodium <1mg, Dietary Fiber 1g*

*Seek the wisdom of
the ages, but look at
the world through
the eyes of a child.
—Ron Wild*

A-Camping We Will Go

Campfire Potatoes

Unforgettable Baked Beans

Marinated Corn Salad

Kerr's Camping Krunch

Blueberry or Pecan Camping Crepes

Peanut Butter Carb Bars

Carob S'mores

Pictured, clockwise from bottom right: Marinated Corn Salad, Unforgettable Baked Beans, Carob S'mores, Peanut Butter Carb Bars, Campfire Potatoes

Unforgettable Baked Beans

⅛ cup canola oil or light olive oil
1¾ cups chopped onion
2 medium cloves garlic, minced
¼ teaspoon salt
½ cup sucanat
⅛ cup dark molasses, not blackstrap
1 cup Classico sun-dried tomato sauce, or favorite
1 can (15 ounces) pineapple tidbits in natural juice, drained
2 cans (16 ounces each) pinto beans, not drained

1. Heat oil in a 12-inch skillet.

2. Add onions, garlic and salt. Sauté onions until dark brown.

3. Add sucanat and molasses and stir well. Add sauce, pineapple and beans, and simmer 45 minutes uncovered on low. Not necessary to bake. Beans are ready when slightly thickened.

Serves 20

Nutrients per serving: Calories 96, Protein 3g, Carbohydrate 16g, Fat 2g, Cholesterol 0mg, Saturated Fat 0g, Sodium 318mg, Dietary Fiber <1g

Campfire Potatoes

5 medium red potatoes, peeling optional, thinly sliced
1 medium onion, thinly sliced
¼ cup canola oil or light olive oil
1 envelope Campbell's onion soup mix
¼ cup minced fresh parsley, packed into measuring cup
1 tablespoon vegetarian Worcestershire sauce
1 cup water
1 teaspoon McKay's chicken-style seasoning
¾ teaspoon salt
Heavy-duty aluminum foil

1. Put potatoes, onion, oil and soup mix into a gallon-sized reclosable plastic bag. Shake well to coat potatoes.

2. Add remaining ingredients and shake well to mix all.

3. Using a double layer of foil, pull out about 25 inches. Fold up sides and ends slightly before putting potatoes in the center.

4. Spread the potatoes evenly on the foil. Pull up sides and seal together. Roll up ends tightly.

5. Roast covered in coals for about 1 hour, or until potatoes are tender, or bake in oven at 350 degrees F for 1 hour and 10 minutes. Serve hot.

Serves 8

Nutrients per serving: Calories 223, Protein 4g, Carbohydrate 37g, Fat 7g, Cholesterol 0mg, Saturated Fat <1g, Sodium 725mg, Dietary Fiber 4g

Marinated
CORN SALAD

2 cans (15 ounces each) corn, drained,
    or 3 cups fresh
1 medium red pepper, diced small
2 green onions, green part, diced
½ cup celery, chopped fine
¼ cup fresh lemon juice
⅛ cup canola oil
⅛ cup parsley, chopped and packed into
    measuring cup
¼ teaspoon garlic powder
2 tablespoons honey

Mix all together in a bowl. Let marinate 8 hours
for best flavor. Serve cold.

Serves 8

Nutrients per serving: Calories 103, Protein 2g,
Carbohydrate 19g, Fat 3g, Cholesterol 0mg,
Saturated Fat 0g, Sodium 11mg, Dietary Fiber 2g

Kerr's
CAMPING KRUNCH

Make this trail mix with your favorite healthful
munchies.

1 cup Sunspire carob chips
1 cup peanuts, raw
1 cup almonds
1 cup raisins
1 cup unsweetened large coconut shreds

Mix, bag and hike!

Rain, rain, go away,
Come again
another day!
—Nursery rhyme

A RECIPE FOR STRESS RELIEF
Growing up in the Pacific Northwest allowed us kids
many camping and hiking opportunities. One of my
favorite places in the United States is Mt. Rainier National
Forest. That is my mountain. I don't know of anything
more stress-relieving than viewing its awesome beauty up
close. My favorite campground is still Ohana Pekosh State
Park inside the Mt. Rainier National Forest. Be sure to visit
it for me!

Blueberry or Pecan
CAMPING CREPES

*And God said,
See, I have given you
every herb that yields
seed which is on the face
of all the earth, and
every tree whose fruit
yields seed; to you it
shall be for food.
—Genesis 1:29*

CREPES:
1 cup whole-wheat pastry flour
1 cup rolled oats
³⁄₈ teaspoon (¼ + ⅛) salt
2 cups vanilla-flavored almond milk,
  or soy milk
1 tablespoon canola oil
⅛ cup honey
1½ tablespoons maple flavoring

1. Put above ingredients into a blender and blend until smooth, about 3 to 4 minutes.

2. Spray a 12-inch skillet with oil. Heat.

3. Pour scant ¼ cup of batter into heated pan.

4. When crepe looks dry, turn and cook on other side. Fold each crepe in half as you remove it from the pan.

5. Fill each crepe with a teaspoon of the desired filling and serve hot.

PECAN FILLING:
½ cup pecans or almonds
¼ cup pure maple syrup

Blend to a thick paste. Tastes wonderful!

BLUEBERRY FILLING:
Polaner all-fruit blueberry jam

Sweet and delicious. Easy, too!

Makes 18 crepes

Peanut Butter
CARB BARS

These are great energy bars for the backpackers in the family.

1 cup brown rice syrup
¾ cup all-natural creamy peanut butter
2¼ cups Grape Nuts cereal

1. In a saucepan, bring brown rice syrup and peanut butter to a low boil, stirring constantly.

2. Heat to 250 degrees F, being careful not to scorch syrup.

3. Remove from heat and stir in Grape Nuts.

4. Line a cookie sheet with oil-sprayed foil.

5. Oil your hands or the bottom of a glass bowl, and carefully pat mixture into a rectangle a little less than ½ inch thick. Recipe will not fill cookie sheet.

6. Allow to cool for 10 minutes before cutting into 1- or 2-inch squares. You must cut them while they are warm.

Serves 20

Nutrients per serving: Calories 137, Protein 4g, Carbohydrate 21g, Fat 5g, Cholesterol 0mg, Saturated Fat 1g, Sodium 135mg, Dietary Fiber 1g

Carob
S'MORES

Make ahead and take these camping with you.

¾ cup brown rice syrup
1 cup Chatfield's dairy-free carob chips or favorite brand
½ teaspoon vanilla
1 box all-natural honey grahams

1. In a saucepan, bring syrup, chips and vanilla to a low boil until you reach 250 degrees F, about 5 minutes, stirring constantly.

2. Allow to cool to 125 degrees F. Working quickly, spread carob sauce on one large graham cracker and top with another cracker, making a sandwich.

3. Put on foil-lined or parchment-lined cookie sheet. Can cool in refrigerator to set the filling. Store in airtight container. Separate the layers with waxed paper.

Makes 16 squares

Nutrients per serving: Calories 120, Protein 2.5g, Carbohydrate 18g, Fat 5g, Cholesterol 0mg, Saturated Fat 2g, Sodium 119mg, Dietary Fiber .5g

Good and upright is the Lord. He guides the humble in what is right and teaches them His way.
—Psalm 25:8-9

Here's To Dad

Manly Marinade

Grilled Tofu

Grilled Vegetables

10 W 30 Italian Marinade

Fresh Blueberry Squares with Nut Crust
and Tofu Whipped Cream

Leo's Carob Cake
with German Sweet Carob Icing

Country Lemonade

Pictured, clockwise from top: Country Lemonade,
Fresh Blueberry Squares, Pecan Almond Cookie,
Grilled Tofu, Grilled Vegetables

Manly MARINADE

You can also use this as a salad dressing.

¼ **cup water**
¼ **cup extra-virgin olive oil**
⅛ **cup lemon juice, fresh**
¼ **cup onion, packed into cup**
1 **small clove garlic**
1 **tablespoon honey**
⅛ **teaspoon salt**
1½ **teaspoon Bill's Best Chik Nish**
  seasoning
1 **tablespoon tahini**
⅛ **teaspoon cayenne (optional)**

Blend all ingredients until well liquefied.

Makes about 1 cup.

SHARING THE COOKING

For years, Bill has refused to teach me how to run the grill. I actually like having no responsibility when it comes to grilling recipes! It gives me a break in the kitchen and makes entertaining more enjoyable.

Grilled TOFU

1 **pound extra-firm, water-packed tofu**
Lawry's seasoned salt
1 **recipe marinade (recipe at left)**

1. Cut tofu into 1 x ½-inch pieces.

2. In a gallon-sized reclosable plastic bag, combine tofu and marinade. Allow to sit for several hours or use immediately.

3. Fold up the edges of a 12 x 15-inch piece of heavy-duty foil and place on the grill. Spray with vegetable oil. Pour marinade and tofu onto the foil; spread out evenly. Sprinkle with seasoned salt.

4. Turn grill on high and allow marinade to cook down and begin to caramelize. Turn the tofu to keep from sticking. Continue to cook down and brown on all sides. The marinade eventually disappears completely.

Serves 5

Nutrients per serving (data includes tofu and marinade): Calories 218, Protein 11g, Carbohydrate 7g, Fat 17g, Cholesterol 0mg, Saturated Fat 2g, Sodium 357mg, Dietary Fiber <1g

Grilled VEGETABLES

Try not to grill more than you will eat. This recipe is best served immediately, not as leftovers.

2 small zucchini, cut lengthwise into ½-inch strips and then in half
2 small summer squash, prepared like zucchini
2 large portobello mushrooms, cut into ½-inch strips
1 large onion, cut into ½-inch rounds
2 medium carrots, peeled and sliced lengthwise into ¼-inch strips
1 yellow pepper, cut into ¾-inch strips
1 red pepper, cut into ¾-inch strips
Seasoned salt
Italian marinade (recipe at right)
Heavy-duty extra-wide foil

1. Wash and prepare vegetables.

2. Pull out two long sheets of foil, about the length of your arm. Double the foil and fold up the edges slightly.

3. Distribute vegetables evenly over foil. Pour one recipe of Italian marinade over the veggies, and salt to taste. Pull the foil together and seal along the top and on the sides.

4. Place the vegetables on the top rack of your grill to steam. If you are cooking tofu, you can steam the veggies while the tofu cooks. Allow to steam about 20 minutes.

5. Open foil along the top and place a few vegetables at a time directly on the grill. Turn over and make grill lines on the other side too. Serve hot.

Serves 20

Nutrients per serving (data includes vegetables and marinade: Calories 78, Protein 1g, Carbohydrate 7g, Fat 6g, Cholesterol 0mg, Saturated Fat <1g, Sodium 172mg, Dietary Fiber 2g

10 W 30 ITALIAN MARINADE

This recipe can be used as a marinade or as a salad dressing.

½ cup extra-virgin olive oil
½ cup water
½ cup lemon juice, fresh
1 tablespoon vegetarian Worcestershire sauce
1 tablespoon honey
1 tablespoon minced dried onions
1 large clove garlic, pressed
½ teaspoon salt
½ teaspoon oregano
¼ teaspoon red pepper seeds (optional)

Put all ingredients in a salad shaker and mix well. Do not blend in a blender.

Makes about 2 cups.

It's a wonderful feeling when your father becomes not a god but a man to you— when he comes down from the mountain and you see he's this man with weaknesses. And you love him as this whole being, not as a figurehead.
—Robin Williams

Fresh BLUEBERRY SQUARES

As water reflects a face, so a man's heart reflects the man.
—Proverbs 27:19

½ cup whole-wheat pastry flour
1 cup 100 percent grape juice frozen
   concentrate
1 cup water
¼ cup canola oil
1 teaspoon vanilla
3 cups fresh blueberries
Salt
1 nut crust (recipe at right)
Tofu whipped cream (recipe at right)

1. In a medium saucepan, whisk whole-wheat flour into juice concentrate, water and canola oil and bring to a boil. Mixture thickens as it boils. Let cool, then stir in vanilla, berries and a pinch of salt.

2. Pour into a cooled nut crust in a 9 by 9-inch or an 8 by 8-inch pan. Top with whipped cream and refrigerate for 2 hours before serving.

Serves 16

Nutrients per serving (data includes nut crust and topping): Calories 235, Protein 4g, Carbohydrate 28g, Fat 13g, Cholesterol 0mg, Saturated Fat <1g, Sodium 88mg, Dietary Fiber 2g

Nut CRUST

⅔ cup pecan meal
⅔ cup whole-wheat pastry flour
Salt
⅛ cup pure maple syrup
⅛ cup canola oil
½ teaspoon pure vanilla extract
½ teaspoon almond extract

1. Stir together the pecan meal, flour and a pinch of salt.

2. Whisk together syrup, canola oil, vanilla extract and almond extract in a separate bowl. Add to the dry ingredients and form a moist crumble.

3. Press into bottom of an oiled 9 x 9-inch square pan. Roll flat.

4. Bake at 375 degrees F for 12 to 14 minutes or until lightly brown. Do not overbake.

Tofu WHIPPED CREAM

This whipped topping is dense, like pudding. You can add a cup of your favorite fresh fruit and blend to make a fruited cream, then layer with granola (page 98) to make a parfait.

2 cups firm silken tofu
3 tablespoons canola oil
4 teaspoons water
¼ cup honey
1 teaspoon lemon juice
¼ teaspoon salt
1 tablespoon pure vanilla

Blend until silky smooth. Refrigerate before serving. Good for 3 to 4 days.

Leo's
CAROB CAKE

My last three years of high school I attended Upper Columbia Academy, a boarding school just outside of Spokane, Washington. While there, I fell in love with my first sweetheart, Greg Warren. Because his parents were on staff at the school, I had the privilege of eating at their home on a multitude of occasions, my favorite being Saturday nights. Leonard, Greg's dad, would make carob cake and peach shakes for everyone. It was my very first introduction to carob. It was a little different taste as far as cakes go, but as a teenager I still thought of it as a special treat. To this day, all those carob cakes we ate are some of the fondest memories of boarding school that I have.

On April 10, 2000, Leonard was killed in an automobile accident on a snow-covered road in New York. This slight adaptation of his recipe is shared in loving memory of a gentle man who truly lived to serve others and his God. Thank you, Leonard, for your Godly and fatherly example. You will be missed.

CAROB CAKE:
¾ cup whole-wheat pastry flour
¾ cup unbleached white flour
½ cup carob powder
¾ cup milled cane sugar
⅓ cup canola oil
1 cup water
1 tablespoon lemon juice
1 tablespoon pure vanilla
¾ teaspoon salt
1 tablespoon Rumford's aluminum-free
    baking
    powder

1. Spoon flours into measuring cup, level off. Sift carob powder and add to flour. Stir in cane sugar, oil, water, lemon juice, vanilla, salt and baking powder. Batter will be slightly thin.

2. Pour into an oiled and floured 8 x 8-inch square baking dish. Bake at 350 degrees F for 30 to 35 minutes. Toothpick inserted should come out clean. Cake does not need to be cool to ice. This cake is also delicious served without icing.

GERMAN SWEET CAROB FROSTING:

½ cup Hokan Lite coconut milk, divided
2 tablespoons cornstarch
1 cup sucanat
½ cup shredded, unsweetened coconut
¼ cup canola oil
½ cup walnuts, chopped

1. In a small bowl stir 2 to 3 tablespoons of the coconut milk into cornstarch until dissolved.

2. In a small saucepan combine the rest of the coconut milk, sucanat, coconut, oil and the cornstarch mixture. Bring to a rapid boil, stirring constantly until slightly thickened, 5 or 6 minutes.

3. Remove from heat and stir in nuts. Ice cake while warm. Icing thickens as it cools.

Success has nothing to do with what you gain in life or accomplish for yourself. Success is what you do for others.
—Danny Thomas

Country
LEMONADE

1 can 100 percent white grape juice
    frozen concentrate
4 cans water
2 cups fresh lemon juice
1 lemon sliced into rounds
    for garnish on glasses

Mix all ingredients together and serve cold.

Serves 8

Nutrients per serving: Calories 135, Protein <1g, Carbohydrate 36g, Fat 0g, Cholesterol 0mg, Saturated Fat 0g, Sodium 6mg, Dietary Fiber <1g

Fourth of July Picnic

Pimento Cheese Block

Taco Salad

French Dressing

Great Picnic Burgers

Relish Caddy

Barb's Waldorf Salad

Red, White & Blue Dessert

Watermelon Punch Bowl with Citrus Cartwheels

Limeade

Pictured, clockwise from bottom left: Relish Caddy;
Limeade; Red, White & Blue Dessert; Great Picnic
Burgers; Barb's Waldorf Salad; Taco Salad

Pimento
CHEESE BLOCK

What we obtain too cheaply we esteem too lightly; it is dearness only that gives everything its value.
—Thomas Paine

1½ cups water
5 envelopes (2½ teaspoons each) Emes unflavored, unsweetened gelatin
¾ cup cashew pieces or meal
1¼ teaspoons salt
2 teaspoons onion powder
¼ teaspoon garlic powder
3 tablespoons brewer's yeast flakes
½ cup (4 ounces) pimentos, not drained
2½ tablespoons lemon juice
2 teaspoons honey
1 teaspoon dill weed

1. Put water, gelatin and cashews into blender and blend to smooth. Add rest of ingredients and blend till smooth again.

2. Pour into a 3-quart saucepan and bring to a low boil, stirring constantly. Mixture will thicken.

3. Remove from heat and allow to cool. I pour half of the mixture into a small square mold and refrigerate for slicing. I pour the other half of the cheese into a plastic-lined square mold and freeze for shredding. This cheese becomes liquid again if heated. When unmolding cheese, hold mold in hot water for about 30 seconds, then turn out onto plate. Shred frozen cheese, and keep stored in freezer until ready to use.

Serves 20

Nutrients per serving: Calories 44, Protein 2g, Carbohydrate 5g, Fat 2g, Cholesterol 0mg, Saturated Fat <1g, Sodium 137mg, Dietary Fiber 1g

Taco
SALAD

1 head iceberg lettuce, cut small
2 medium tomatoes, diced small
1 can (15 ounces) black beans, drained and rinsed
½ cup black olives, cut into rings (optional)
1 bag (10.3 ounces) corn chips
1½ cups shredded pimento cheese block (recipe at left), or Veggie Shreds imitation cheese
1 cup French dressing (recipe follows)

Keep ingredients separate until just before serving. Toss together in a very large bowl. This salad does *not* keep once the chips are soggy. If I am making this salad and I know there will be leftovers, I let everyone add their own chips.

Serves 20

Nutrients per serving: Calories 200, Protein 5g, Carbohydrate 23g, Fat 10g, Cholesterol 0mg, Saturated Fat 2g, Sodium 352mg, Dietary Fiber 3.5g

French
DRESSING

⅜ cup (¼ + ⅛) canola oil
½ teaspoon paprika
⅓ cup raw honey
¼ cup sweet onion
½ teaspoon salt, or to taste
1 large clove garlic
¼ cup fresh lemon juice
2 cups cubed, vine-ripened tomatoes

Blend all ingredients in blender until smooth. Can be stored in refrigerator 7 to 10 days.

Makes 24 one-ounce servings

Nutrients per serving: Calories 47, Protein 0g, Carbohydrate 4g, Fat 3g, Cholesterol 0mg, Saturated Fat 0g, Sodium 47mg, Dietary Fiber <1g

Great
PICNIC BURGERS

½ pound extra-firm tofu, crumbled
1 cup instant potato flakes
1 cup cooked millet (recipe, below right),
  or cooked Malt-o-Meal
⅓ cup rolled oats
⅓ cup fine yellow corn meal
1 tablespoon dark molasses
¼ teaspoon garlic powder
2 teaspoons fresh parsley, chopped
1 teaspoon fresh basil, chopped
  or ½ teaspoon dried
1 tablespoon minced dried onions
1 tablespoon liquid aminos
1 tablespoon McKay's chicken-style
  seasoning
½ teaspoon salt

FOR FRYING:
¼ cup extra light olive oil or canola oil
1 tablespoon vegetarian Worcestershire sauce
Yellow corn meal, fine

1. Mash tofu. Mix rest of burger ingredients into tofu, making a fine crumble. Mixture should be moist but not wet.

2. Pack mixture into ¼ cup measure. Sprinkle a layer of corn meal onto a plate and press mixture into shape. Turn burger over and press into corn meal, making sure both sides are coated well. Shape all burgers before frying.

3. Heat oil in a 12-inch skillet. Add Worcestershire sauce all at once and immediately cover pan. Wait for popping to stop. Add burgers and fry to a golden brown on each side, about five minutes each side. Serve hot. These freeze well.

Variations :

Try making black bean burgers (page 73) or lentil burgers by replacing the 1 cup of cooked millet with your favorite refried bean. Can also use cooked split peas. When substituting make sure your beans are in a mashed consistency.

Serves 10

Nutrients per serving: Calories 135, Protein 5g, Carbohydrate 19g, Fat 5g, Cholesterol 0mg, Saturated Fat <1g, Sodium 365mg, Dietary Fiber 3g

Relish
CADDY

Make a colorful caddy to hold the condiments at your next picnic. Your guests will love this simple creation!

1 red pepper
1 yellow pepper
1 green pepper
V-shaped cutter
Ketchup
Mustard
Relish

1. Select peppers that are all about the same size and hardy-looking. Also, make sure they will sit up on their own. Wash and pat dry.

2. Using a v-shaped cutter, begin making cuts quite close to the stem end of the peppers. Continue around evenly in a circle connecting each cut. Pop the top off of the pepper and discard.

3. Remove the seeds from inside and rinse. You can store the peppers in ice water until ready to use.

4. Fill the red pepper with catsup, the yellow with mustard, and the green with relish. You can find healthful versions of condiments in your local health food store.

5. Line a plate with leaf lettuce. Place filled peppers on the lettuce.

MAKING COOKED MILLET

Bring 1½ cups distilled water to a boil in a small saucepan. Add ½ cup millet and ⅛ teaspoon salt. Cover and bring to a boil again. Turn heat to low and cook about 30 minutes. Stir and add 1 to 2 tablespoons of water. Cook for another 30 minutes, checking every 10 minutes and adding just a touch of water if necessary. Even though millet absorbs its water very early on in the cooking process, it will be gritty if it is not cooked for 1 hour.

You gain strength, courage, and confidence by every experience in which you really stop to look fear in the face. You are able to say to yourself, "I lived through this horror. I can take the next thing that comes along."
—Eleanor Roosevelt

Barb's
WALDORF SALAD

The health of nations is more important than the wealth of nations.
—Will Durant

2 cups cooked barley (½ cup dry, cooked in 2 cups water)
1 teaspoon canola oil
⅛ teaspoon salt
1 can (15 ounces) pineapple tidbits in unsweetened pineapple juice, drained, reserving liquid
¼ cup shredded, unsweetened coconut
⅓ cup pecans, coarsely chopped
2 medium Granny Smith apples, peeled, cored and chopped into small pieces

1. Rinse barley and put in 2-quart saucepan. Add 1 teaspoon oil and dextrinize grain by lightly browning it for 3 to 5 minutes.

2. Add 2 cups boiling distilled water to grain. Stir, cover and simmer on low 35 minutes.

3. Add salt and cook 10 more minutes. Make sure all moisture has cooked into the barley. Put cooked barley in bowl and mix in pineapple pieces, coconut, pecans and apples. Make sure to measure your cooked barley, as this makes a little more than 2 cups cooked.

DRESSING:
Reserved pineapple juice plus enough water to make 1 cup liquid
1 envelope (2.7 ounces) Sovex Instead of Yogurt dessert mix, piña colada flavor
2 tablespoons honey

1. Whisk together and let stand 15 minutes before mixing into above barley mixture.

2. Chill salad 2 to 3 hours before serving or make day ahead. Serve cold.

Serves 12

Nutrients per serving: Calories 148, Protein 1g, Carbohydrate 31g, Fat 3g, Cholesterol 0mg, Saturated Fat <1g, Sodium 38mg, Dietary Fiber 3g

Red, White & Blue
DESSERT

2 boxes (12.3 ounces) extra-firm silken Mori-Nu tofu
6 tablespoons water, divided
2 packages (3.85 ounces each) Mori-Nu Mates vanilla pudding mix
½ teaspoon almond extract
1 envelope (2½ teaspoons) Emes unflavored, unsweetened gelatin
2 pounds fresh blueberries
2 pounds fresh strawberries, halved

1. In a blender, blend 1 box of the tofu with 3 tablespoons of the water to creamy.

2. Add 1 package of the pudding, almond extract and Emes gelatin. Blend until smooth and sugars dissolve, about 4 minutes. Pour into another bowl.

3. Blend remaining water with tofu to smooth. Add remaining pudding mix and blend to smooth. Mix well with first batch of pudding.

4. Wash berries. Set aside ½ cup of blueberries and 12 to 15 strawberries for garnish. Cut tops off of remaining strawberries, and slice in half from top to bottom. Bigger berries can be quartered.

To assemble:

Put ½ cup of the pudding in the bottom of a 4-quart clear glass bowl. Layer with half of the blueberries, then half of the strawberries. Next, spread 1¼ cup pudding over the berries. Won't completely cover. Layer rest of blueberries, then strawberries (saving those set aside for the garnish), and top with remaining pudding. Arrange ½ cup blueberries in the top left corner of the "flag" forming the "stars." Next make 4 rows of stripes with the remaining strawberry halves. Allow to chill thoroughly before serving.

Serves 24

Nutrients per serving: Calories 54, Protein 2g, Carbohydrate 11g, Fat <1g, Cholesterol 0mg, Saturated Fat 0g, Sodium 22mg, Dietary Fiber 2g

Watermelon
PUNCH BOWL

After you've scooped out the watermelon to make your punch bowl, you can eat the contents as is, or turn it into watermelon sorbet (page 77). Fill your new punch bowl and float some citrus cartwheels (recipe at right) on your punch as a beautiful garnish!

1 medium, slightly oval watermelon
Large rubber band
Ballpoint pen
V-shaped cutter
Large knife
Scoop for removing watermelon

1. Carefully take a thin slice off the bottom of your watermelon so it will sit flat for you. If you take too much off the bottom of the melon it will leak.

2. Place your rubber band around the watermelon, raising it about an inch above the center. Use your rubber band as a guideline to draw a circle around the melon. Remove the rubber band.

3. Place the tip of your v-shaped cutter on the line you've drawn. Press in firmly. Continue around the melon with the v-shaped cutter, connecting each cut.

4. Taking a large knife, cut into the top of the melon splitting it across the top. This will allow you to separate the top from the bottom more easily.

5. Using a scoop, remove the pulp from the melon, being careful to leave about ¾ inch of pink around all the edges.

Citrus
CARTWHEELS

Float on the top of your favorite punch.

Lemons, limes, grapefruits or oranges
Citrus zester/scorer
Sharp knife or garnisher

Holding your citrus fruit firmly, begin at one end of your fruit and press the scorer into the flesh of the rind. Pull the scorer towards the other end of the fruit while turning it at the same time. Continue in this fashion until you have made about 5 or 6 score marks. Now cut the fruit in round, thin slices.

Most folks are about as happy as they make up their minds to be.
—*Abraham Lincoln*

Lime
ADE

Beautiful served in a watermelon punch bowl.

1 can (12 ounces) Welch's white grape
frozen concentrate, 100 percent juice
4 cans of water
1 cup lime juice, fresh-squeezed

Mix all together. Serve cold.

Serves 8

Nutrients per serving: Calories 128, Protein 0g, Carbohydrate 34g, Fat 0g, Cholesterol 0mg, Saturated Fat 0g, Sodium 6mg, Dietary Fiber 0g

HAPPY BIRTHDAY, BABY!

WARM CAROB-RASPBERRY PUDDING CAKE

FRUIT PIZZA WITH AN
OATMEAL COOKIE CRUST,
PEANUT MAPLE CREAM AND
CARAMEL TOPPING

PEANUT BUTTER OAT CUPS

PEACH SHAKE & ICE CREAM

PIÑA COLADA SHAKE & ICE CREAM

Pictured, clockwise from bottom left: Peanut Butter Oat
Cups, Piña Colada Ice Cream, Fruit Pizza, Peach Shake,
Warm Carob-Raspberry Pudding Cake

Warm Carob
RASPBERRY PUDDING CAKE

This cake is baked in its own frosting and is very dense and moist. Delicious!

FROSTING:
⅜ cup (¼ + ⅛) **Sunspire vegan or Chatfield's dairy-free carob chips**
½ cup **seedless raspberry or blackberry all-fruit jam**
½ cup **Hokan Lite coconut milk**

CAKE:
½ cup **boiling water**
⅓ cup and 2 teaspoons **carob powder**
¼ cup **Hokan Lite coconut milk**
1 teaspoon **pure vanilla**
⅓ cup **seedless raspberry or blackberry all-fruit jam**
¼ cup **water**
⅓ cup **sucanat**
½ cup **instant potato flakes**
½ cup **canola oil**
1 cup **whole-wheat pastry flour**
1½ teaspoon **Rumford's aluminum-free baking powder**
¼ teaspoon **salt**
Fresh raspberries for garnish

My Aunt Barbie taught me how to peel carrots and grind grain into flour. We make yummy cakes in my Easy Bake Oven too.
—Katie Brewer, age 6

For the frosting:

1. In a small saucepan bring chips, jam and coconut milk to a simmer, stirring occasionally until smooth.

2. Pour hot frosting into an oiled 8-inch round cake pan. (An 8 x 8-inch square pan will work too). Set aside.

For the batter:

1. In a medium bowl whisk together the boiling water and carob powder. Add coconut milk, vanilla and jam. Set aside.

2. In a saucepan, bring to a boil ¼ cup water and sucanat. Add potato flakes and let sit for 2 minutes. With a mixer, beat in oil. Set aside.

3. In a small bowl mix flour, baking powder and salt together.

4. Add flour and potato mixture to the carob mixture. Beat at medium speed until creamy. Pour and spread batter evenly over frosting mixture, and bake in the middle of the oven at 350 degrees F for 40 to 45 minutes or until tester comes out clean. (Remember frosting will still be liquid at the very bottom.)

5. Cool cake 2 minutes. Run knife around cake and invert onto plate. Garnish top with raspberries. (Do not wait until cake is cool to invert.) Cut into narrow wedges to serve.

Serves 10

Nutrients per serving: Calories 302, Protein 3g, Carbohydrate 47g, Fat 15g, Cholesterol 0mg, Saturated Fat 2.5g, Sodium 133mg, Dietary Fiber 3g

Fruit PIZZA

This is a beautiful dessert pizza that kids really like.

OATMEAL COOKIE CRUST:
1 cup pure maple syrup
2 teaspoons pure vanilla
¾ teaspoon salt
½ cup canola oil
2¼ cups quick oats, blended into flour
2 cups whole-wheat pastry flour

PEANUT MAPLE CREAM:
1½ cups peanut butter (16-ounce jar)
¾ cup pure maple syrup

ASSORTED FRESH FRUIT:
1 large Granny Smith Apple, peeled, cored and sliced thin
3 kiwi, peeled and sliced into thin rounds
1 cup blueberries or favorite fresh fruit (strawberries, raspberries, grapes, nuts, peaches; any fruit toppings you like)

CARAMEL TOPPING:
⅓ cup sucanat
2 tablespoons water

For the cookie crust:

1. In a medium mixing bowl beat together the pure maple syrup, vanilla, salt and oil; add oat and pastry flours. Let sit 5 to 10 minutes to thicken slightly.

2. With oiled hands, spread out dough on an oiled 15-inch round baking stone or pizza pan. (Can make square pizzas too). Bake at 350 degrees F for 25 to 30 minutes or until very lightly browning around edges. Cool completely.

To assemble:

1. Beat together maple cream ingredients until smooth. Spread over cooled cookie crust. Top with sliced fruit.

2. In a small saucepan over medium heat, bring the caramel ingredients to a boil. Using a candy thermometer bring the sucanat to 250 degrees F, stirring occasionally. Immediately drizzle over the fruit. Turns to caramel instantly. Serve immediately.

Tip: Cut fruit just before serving so it doesn't discolor. The caramel will liquefy again after several hours, so it does not make good leftovers.

Serves 20

Nutrients per serving: Calories 362, Protein 9g, Carbohydrate 47g, Fat 18g, Cholesterol 0mg, Saturated Fat 3g, Sodium 219mg, Dietary Fiber 4g

Grown-ups never understand anything for themselves, and it is tiresome for children to be always and forever explaining things to them.
—Antoine De Saint-Exupery

THE FRESHEST PRODUCE

When choosing fruits and vegetables for recipes, always pick fresh, firm produce that is brightly colored and free from bruises.

Peanut Butter
OAT CUPS

This recipe makes a great hors d'oeuvre to serve at any party!

DOUGH:
½ cup Chatfield's carob chips
2¼ cups quick oats
½ cup whole-wheat pastry flour
½ teaspoon salt
⅓ cup canola oil
½ cup and ⅛ cup sucanat
¼ cup water
½ cup all-natural creamy peanut butter

DIP:
½ cup Chatfield's carob chips
¼ cup all-natural creamy peanut butter
2 teaspoons canola oil
1 tablespoon sucanat
36 pecan halves

*Life's a tough
proposition, and the
first hundred years
are the hardest.
—Wilson Mizner*

For the dough:

1. Lightly pulse carob chips in a food processor to break up. Do not turn them into meal.

2. Mix together chips, oats, flour, salt and oil; set aside.

3. In a saucepan bring the water and sucanat to a low boil for 1 minute. Turn off heat and stir in peanut butter. Cool and add to above mixture; stir to combine.

4. Using a 1-tablespoon scoop, fill 36 oil-sprayed mini-muffin cups. Press down dough. Bake at 350 degrees F for about 12 minutes or until lightly brown around edges. Allow to cool in the pan for 3 or 4 minutes. Remove to cooling rack.

For the dip:

1. In a small saucepan, melt together carob chips, peanut butter, oil and sucanat.

2. Holding oat cups by the top, dip bottoms in carob sauce coming ¼ inch up the sides. Lay carob side facing up, and place a pecan half on each oat cup.

Makes about 36 oat cups, 1 tablespoon each

Nutrients per serving: Calories 128, Protein 3g, Carbohydrate 12g, Fat 8g, Cholesterol 0mg, Saturated Fat 1g, Sodium 51mg, Dietary Fiber 1g

Peach
SHAKE OR ICE CREAM

SHAKE:
1 can (13.5 ounces) Hokan Lite coconut
milk, chilled
3 cups fresh peaches, peeled, sliced and
frozen in two separate plastic bags
OR
2 cans (15 ounces each) peaches in
natural juices, drained and frozen
⅜ cup (¼ + ⅛) Welch's 100 percent
white grape peach juice, frozen
concentrate

Place all in blender and blend to smooth. Serve
immediately.

Makes 3 eight-ounce servings

Nutrients per serving: Calories 210, Protein 1g,
Carbohydrate 38g, Fat 7g, Cholesterol 0mg,
Saturated Fat 7g, Sodium 20mg, Dietary Fiber 3g

ICE CREAM:
Increase white grape peach juice
concentrate to ½ cup
Other ingredients, same as above

Blend until smooth. Pour into ice cube trays and
freeze. In your food processor, process the ice
cream cubes into ice cream. Serve immediately.

Makes 6 half-cup servings

Nutrients per serving: Calories 115, Protein 1g,
Carbohydrate 21g, Fat 3.5g, Cholesterol 0mg,
Saturated Fat 3g, Sodium 12mg, Dietary Fiber 1g

Piña Colada
SHAKE OR ICE CREAM

SHAKE:
3 cups fresh pineapple, cut into 1-inch
cubes and frozen
1 can (13.5 ounces) Hokan Lite coconut
milk, chilled
⅛ cup coconut, shredded, unsweetened
⅜ cup (¼ + ⅛) Welch's 100 percent white
grape juice, frozen concentrate

Blend all in blender until smooth. Serve immediately. (Freeze pineapple in 2 separate plastic
sandwich bags.)

Makes 3 eight-ounce servings

Nutrients per serving: Calories 232, Protein 1g,
Carbohydrate 40g, Fat 9g, >Cholesterol 0mg,
Saturated Fat 8g, Sodium 32mg, Dietary Fiber 2g

ICE CREAM:
Increase white grape juice concentrate to
½ cup
Other ingredients, same as above

Blend; pour into ice cube trays and freeze. In a
food processor, process until smooth. Serve
immediately.

Makes 6 half-cup servings

Nutrients per serving: Calories 126, Protein <1g,
Carbohydrate 23g, Fat 4g, Cholesterol 0mg,
Saturated Fat 4g, Sodium 18mg, Dietary Fiber 1g

It's no secret—
the people who live
long are those
who long to live.
—Unknown

Sumptuous Summer Soups & Sandwiches

Soups:

Roasted Gazpacho

Aunt Lois' Fruit Soup

Cream of Broccoli

Lemon Asparagus Soup

Potato Dill Soup

Chilled Raspberry-Peach Soup

Cheesy Dill Soup

Sandwiches:

Pecan-Olive Spread

Grilled Pimento Cheese Sandwich

Black Bean Burgers

Pictured: Chilled Raspberry-Peach Soup

Roasted GAZPACHO

This soup is excellent served hot or cold.

1 large jalapeño, seeded (use ½ jalapeño
   for milder taste), optional
2 large cloves garlic, skin on
4 large ripe tomatoes, quartered
2 sweet red onions, quartered
1 sweet red pepper, seeded
4 to 5 tablespoons olive oil, divided
4 ears fresh sweet corn (to make 2 cups
   kernels)
1 large cucumber, divided and diced
¼ cup fresh basil leaves
1½ teaspoons salt
3 tablespoons lime juice, divided
½ cup chopped black olives (garnish
   only)

1. Preheat oven to 450 degrees. Put jalapeño if using, garlic, tomatoes, onions and pepper into a roasting pan and dribble about 2 tablespoons of the oil over them. Roast in the oven 30 to 40 minutes, removing the garlic after 10 so it won't scorch.

2. Turn the vegetables over after 15 to 20 minutes. When done the vegetables will look browned in places and wilted.

3. Remove husks from corn and brush with remaining oil. Turn oven to broil. Broil corn, turning once until it begins to brown slightly. Depending on your broiler this can take anywhere from 5 to 20 minutes.

4. Remove from oven. When cool enough to handle, cut kernels off the cobs. Set aside 1 cup of kernels for the soup, and set aside the rest for garnish.

5. When roasted vegetables are cool enough to handle, process in batches in a blender or food processor, but leave chunky. Don't make this smooth! Add 1 cup of corn kernels, ½ of the

cucumber, basil, salt and 2 tablespoons of the lime juice to your vegetable mixture as you are blending the batches.

6. Mix the finished soup together well. Adjust salt if necessary. Chill thoroughly.

7. Mix the remaining 1 tablespoon lime juice into the reserved cucumbers.

8. When ready to serve, garnish the top of each bowl with a spoonful of the remaining corn kernels, black olives and diced cucumbers.

Serves 8

Nutrients per serving: Calories 137, Protein 3g, Carbohydrate 21g, Fat 6g, Cholesterol 0mg, Saturated Fat 1g, Sodium 449mg, Dietary Fiber 4g

Potato DILL SOUP

3 cups water
4 teaspoons vegetable boullion
1½ cup onion, chopped
2 cups potatoes, sliced or diced
2 to 3 tablespoons chopped fresh dill,
   or 1 tablespoon dried
3 tablespoons olive or canola oil
⅜ cup (¼ + ⅛) whole-wheat pastry flour
1 teaspoon salt
2½ cups favorite soy milk

1. Bring water, boullion, onion, potatoes and dill to a boil. Reduce heat, cover and simmer 10 minutes. Remove from heat.

2. Place ½ to ⅔ of mixture in a blender and blend to puree. Please use caution when blending anything hot. Add back to chunky mixture.

3. In a saucepan heat oil. Add flour and salt, and whisk until thick and bubbly.

4. Add milk all at once. Bring to a boil and thicken.

5. Whisk into potato mixture and boil. Serve hot.

Makes 10 one-cup servings

Nutrients per serving: Calories 133, Protein 4g, Carbohydrate 18g, Fat 5g, Cholesterol 0mg, Saturated Fat trace, Sodium 273mg, Dietary Fiber 2g

It is not how much we have, but how much we enjoy, that makes happiness.
—Charles Haddon Spurgeon

Chilled Raspberry-
PEACH SOUP

This chilled, two-color soup makes a stunning presentation in a white bowl. If you don't have a strainer for berry seeds, I recommend making the soup with strawberries. It won't need to be strained.

BERRY SOUP:
¾ cup fresh orange juice
3 tablespoons fresh lime juice
⅜ cup (¼ + ⅛) Welch's 100 percent white grape juice frozen concentrate
¼ teaspoon ground cinnamon
⅛ teaspoon ground nutmeg
4 cups fresh or frozen raspberries, strawberries or blackberries, rinsed and drained

PEACH SOUP:
¾ cup fresh orange juice
3 tablespoons fresh lemon juice
3 tablespoons Welch's 100 percent white grape juice frozen concentrate
4 cups fresh peaches, peeled and chopped

1. Place all ingredients for the berry soup in a blender or food processor and process till smooth. Strain out seeds. Cover and chill. Stir before serving.

2. Blend all the ingredients for the peach soup. No need to strain. Cover and chill. Stir before using.

3. When ready to serve, pour berry and peach soups into separate pitchers. Hold a pitcher in each hand. Pour soups simultaneously and slowly into a soup bowl.

4. Repeat procedure with remaining bowls. Using the tip of a paring knife, swirl the knife slowly back and forth through the two colors.

Makes 8 one-cup servings

Nutrients per serving: Calories 146, Protein 2g, Carbohydrate 36g, Fat 1g, Cholesterol 0mg, Saturated Fat 0g, Sodium 1mg, Dietary Fiber 5g

Lemon
ASPARAGUS SOUP

1 medium onion, chopped
¾ cup celery, chopped
½ teaspoons salt
⅛ cup canola oil
2 tablespoons cornstarch
2 teaspoons McKay's chicken-style seasoning
1 cup water
¾ pound fresh asparagus, trimmed and cut into 1-inch pieces
2 cups favorite soy milk
¼ teaspoon grated lemon peel
⅛ teaspoon ground nutmeg
¼ teaspoon seasoned salt

1. In a 2-quart saucepan, sauté onion and celery with salt in oil until lightly browned.

2. Dissolve cornstarch and seasoning in water. Add to the above saucepan. Bring to a boil. The mixture will thicken quickly.

3. Add the asparagus. Reduce heat; cover and simmer until the asparagus is crisp tender, 3 to 4 minutes. The asparagus will turn bright green. Stir in rest of ingredients. Cover and simmer for 5 minutes. Serve immediately. You may cook this soup an additional 15 minutes if you like your asparagus quite soft. I prefer my asparagus not overcooked. It's prettier, too.

Makes 6 one-cup servings

Nutrients per serving: Calories 101, Protein 4g, Carbohydrate 9g, Fat 6g, Cholesterol 0mg, Saturated Fat 1g, Sodium 434mg, Dietary Fiber 1g

A merry heart does good, like medicine. But a broken spirit dries the bones.
—Proverbs 17:22

MAKING SOUPS
Note: I only use pure, distilled water in my soup recipes.

Cheesy Dill Soup

1 cup carrots, finely chopped
¼ cup celery, finely chopped
½ cup onion, finely chopped
1¾ cups water
2½ teaspoons McKay's chicken-style seasoning
2 cups soy milk
¼ cup whole-wheat pastry flour
Paprika
Salt
1 cup pimento cheese sauce (page 16)
⅛ cup fresh dill, chopped
⅛ cup fresh lemon juice

1. Heat carrots, celery, onion, water and seasoning to boiling, then simmer 15 minutes covered.

2. Combine soy milk, flour and a dash of paprika, and stir into chicken broth mixture. Salt to taste. Cook till bubbly and thick. Add cheese, dill and lemon, and mix well.

3. Simmer 5 more minutes and serve hot with whole-wheat croutons sprinkled on top.

Serves 6

Nutrients per serving: Calories 113, Protein 5g, Carbohydrate 14g, Fat 5g, Cholesterol 0mg, Saturated Fat 1g, Sodium 399mg, Dietary Fiber 2g

Cream of Broccoli Soup

3 cups water
4 teaspoons McKay's chicken-style seasoning
1½ cups onion, chopped
4 cups broccoli, finely chopped (use food processor)
2 bay leaves
½ teaspoon salt
Small clove of garlic, minced, or dash of garlic powder
3 tablespoons canola oil
⅜ cup (¼ + ⅛) whole-wheat pastry flour
1 teaspoon salt
2½ cups soy milk

1. Put water, seasoning, onion, broccoli, bay leaves, salt and garlic into a 4-quart stock pot and boil 10 minutes.

2. Remove bay leaves and puree ⅔ of the mixture. Add back to soup. Please use caution when blending hot ingredients.

3. Heat oil; add flour and salt. Whisk to thick and bubbly.

4. Add milk all at once. Bring to a boil and thicken.

5. Whisk into broccoli mixture. Bring to a boil. Serve hot.

Serves 8

Nutrients per serving: Calories 118, Protein 5g, Carbohydrate 12g, Fat 7g, Cholesterol 0mg, Saturated Fat <1g, Sodium 655mg, Dietary Fiber 2.5g

Aunt Lois' FRUIT SOUP

This steaming soup is excellent served with a scoop of vanilla Better Than Ice Creme.

2 cans (32 ounces each) Mountain Sun 100 percent natural apricot nectar
1 cup Minute tapioca
1 bag (16 ounces) frozen strawberries, or 4 cups fresh (slice fresh in half)
1 bag (12 ounces) frozen raspberries, or 3 cups fresh
1 can (16 ounces) fruit cocktail in natural juices, don't drain
1 banana, sliced into ¼-inch slices

1. In a 4-quart Dutch oven, combine juice and tapioca and let sit for 5 minutes.

2. Heat over medium adding the rest of the ingredients, except banana. Bring to a low boil and simmer 15 minutes or until all the tapioca is absorbed.

3. Add banana just before serving.

Makes 15 one-cup servings

Nutrients per serving: Calories 163, Protein 1g, Carbohydrate 41g, Fat 0g, Cholesterol 0mg, Saturated Fat 0g, Sodium 7mg, Dietary Fiber 3g

Black Bean BURGERS

Make picnic burgers (page 59), substituting 1 cup vegetarian refried black beans for the 1 cup of cooked millet. For a spicier variety, try also adding 1 to 2 teaspoons minced jalapeño peppers.

Serves 10

Nutrients per serving: Calories 135, Protein 5g, Carbohydrate 19g, Fat 5g, Cholesterol 0mg, Saturated Fat <1g, Sodium 365mg, Dietary Fiber 3g

Grilled PIMENTO CHEESE SANDWICH

Light olive oil or canola oil
Thinly sliced whole-wheat bread
Garlic salt
Pimento cheese block (page 58)

1. Heat skillet. Lightly brush olive oil on one side of each piece of bread.

2. Lightly sprinkle the garlic salt on the oiled side of each piece of bread.

3. Fry bread in pan to toast on each side without cheese.

4. Remove bread, add a slice of cheese and allow to warm slightly. Cheese melts quickly. Serve immediately.

Serving size: one sandwich

Nutrients per serving: Calories 328, Protein 11g, Carbohydrate 41g, Fat 16g, Cholesterol 0mg, Saturated Fat 2g, Sodium 1089mg, Dietary Fiber 9g

Pecan-Olive SPREAD

Great on toast or crackers or as a sandwich spread.

1 cup firm, water-packed tofu, drained and packed into cup
⅓ cup pecan meal
⅔ cup finely chopped black olives
½ cup finely chopped celery
1¼ teaspoons onion powder
⅛ teaspoon garlic powder
½ teaspoon salt
½ cup Vegenaise

1. In a bowl, mash tofu.

2. Add rest of ingredients and mix well. Chill.

Makes 40 one-tablespoon servings

Nutrients per serving: Calories 41, Protein 1g, Carbohydrate 1g, Fat 4g, Cholesterol 0mg, Saturated Fat .5g, Sodium 81mg, Dietary Fiber 0g

*From a letter:
I have thoroughly enjoyed the recipes that I have tried. And friends and co-workers haven't a clue that they have been eating soybean products or healthy food!*

Summer Desserts & Carob Treats

Pecan-Almond Cookies

Blackberry-Apple Bars

Peanut Butter & Jelly Cookies

Watermelon Sorbet

The Best Carob Fudge Pie

Crunchy Graham Cracker Crust

The Best Carob Fudge

Fudgy Carob Cookies or Mini Muffins

Pictured, clockwise from top: Watermelon Sorbet,
Blackberry-Apple Bars, Peanut Butter & Jelly Cookies,
Pecan-Almond Cookies
Cake stand by Mosaicwares

Pecan-
ALMOND COOKIES

3 cups pecan meal
4 cups whole-wheat pastry flour
¼ teaspoon sea salt
1 cup pure maple syrup
1 teaspoon vanilla
1 tablespoon almond extract
1 cup canola oil

1. Mix together pecan meal, flour and salt.

2. In a separate bowl whisk together syrup, vanilla, almond extract and oil. Combine the two mixtures and stir well.

3. Using a 2-tablespoon scoop, measure dough onto an oiled cookie sheet. Flatten each cookie with the bottom of an oiled glass to ½ inch. Bake at 350 degrees F for 12 to 14 minutes or until cookies feel firm on top and look dry.

4. To freeze, layer in a square container with waxed paper between layers.

Makes 100 one-cookie servings

Nutrients per serving: Calories 88, Protein 1g, Carbohydrate 7g, Fat 7g, Cholesterol 0mg, Saturated Fat <1g, Sodium 6mg, Dietary Fiber 1g

Blackberry-
APPLE BARS

I've listed a few variations below. Polaner has a good variety of all-fruit jams; see what combinations you can come up with.

CRUST:
1 cup whole-wheat pastry flour
½ cup oat bran
2 cups rolled oats
1¼ cup sucanat
¾ cup canola oil

FILLING:
1 cup blackberries, fresh or frozen
1 medium Granny Smith apple, shredded
½ cup all-fruit blackberry jam

1. In a large bowl combine dry ingredients, then stir in oil. Mix well. Set aside 1½ cups crust mixture for topping.

2. Press rest of crust into an oil-sprayed 9 x 13-inch pan.

3. In a separate bowl mix together filling ingredients. Spread evenly over crust. Sprinkle rest of crust mixture on top evenly covering fruit. Pat down gently with your hands.

4. Bake at 350 degrees F for 45 to 55 minutes. Top will begin to brown. When cool cut into 2-inch squares. Do not overbake.

Variations:

Substitute raspberries and raspberry jam for raspberry bars, or blueberries and all-fruit blueberry jam for blueberry bars.

Apricot-raisin bars:

Make filling with 1 cup dried apricots diced small, 1 shredded apple, ½ cup all-fruit apricot jam, and ¼ cup rinsed raisins. Add ½ teaspoon cinnamon to the crust mixture. The apricot bars only need to bake 35 to 40 minutes.

Serves 20

Nutrients per serving: Calories 231, Protein 4g, Carbohydrate 29g, Fat 10g, Cholesterol 0mg, Saturated Fat 1g, Sodium 49mg, Dietary Fiber 4g

Peanut Butter
& Jelly Cookies

These freeze very well, but need to sit out for 24 hours to let the jam set up first. Christmas tip: This dough rolls out well on a floured surface to use with cookie cutters. I spread the jam right on top of the cookies and bake. They come out of the oven already "frosted." Wonderful!

1 cup pure maple syrup
1 teaspoon pure vanilla
¾ teaspoon salt
¾ cup creamy natural peanut butter
¼ cup water
1¼ cups quick oats, ground into flour in a dry blender
2 cups whole-wheat pastry flour
All-fruit berry jam

1. Cream together syrup, vanilla, salt, peanut butter and water.

2. Mix in oat flour and whole-wheat pastry flour.

3. Allow mixture to sit for 10 minutes while the oats absorb the moisture and loose their stickiness.

4. Roll dough into tablespoon-sized balls and place on cookie sheet. Press your thumbprint in the center of each cookie.

5. Spoon ¼ teaspoon seedless blackberry or seedless black raspberry all-fruit jam into each thumbprint. Smuckers and generic jams work great. I don't use Polaner for this recipe; it's too thin.

6. Bake at 350 degrees F for 10 to 12 minutes. Don't overbake.

Serves 50

Nutrients per serving: Calories 76, Protein 2g, Carbohydrate 12g, Fat 2g, Cholesterol 0mg, Saturated Fat <1g, Sodium 51mg, Dietary Fiber 1g

Watermelon
Sorbet

This is one of the best summer treats I have ever eaten.

10 cups seedless watermelon, cubed
½ cup fresh lemon juice
¾ cup Welch's 100 percent white grape juice frozen concentrate

1. Place watermelon 1 to 2 cups at a time in a food processor or blender, and process until smooth. I leave mine a little bit chunky. Repeat with remaining melon and put all in a big bowl.

2. Add lemon juice and concentrate. Stir.

3. Pour mixture into a 9 x 13-inch pan, or a 10 x 14 is even better, and freeze until almost firm. Break up mixture by hand, stirring well, or transfer to a large bowl and beat at medium speed with a mixer until smooth.

4. Return mixture to pan and freeze until firm. Let stand at room temperature for 30 to 60 minutes before serving. May also be frozen in a sorbet freezer.

Serves 20

Nutrients per serving: Calories 51, Protein .5g, Carbohydrate 12g, Fat 0g, Cholesterol 0mg, Saturated Fat 0g, Sodium 2mg, Dietary Fiber trace

Choosing the Best Melons

To test a watermelon for ripeness, look at the color of the ground spot (the part of the melon that rested on the ground). It should be yellow, not white. (Forget thumping the melon, it's not reliable).

To test any small melon for ripeness, press the non-stem end. It should give slightly when medium pressure is applied. Sniff the stem end to check for a smell like sweet ripe fruit. If no scent is detectable, it is not ripe.

—Sandi Brewer

Some people come into our lives and quickly go. Some stay for a while and leave footprints on our hearts, and we are never the same.
—Unknown

The Best
CAROB FUDGE PIE

People tend to think I don't like chocolate. It couldn't be further from the truth! I understand being addicted to chocolate. The theobromine in chocolate is related to caffeine. But switching to carob won't be the end of the world! You can break the addiction and have a great-tasting alternative.

½ cup pure maple syrup
2 teaspoons pure vanilla
1 tablespoon Roma (noncaffeinated coffee substitute)
1 box (12.3 ounces) of firm Mori-Nu silken tofu
3 cups Sunspire carob chips
Graham cracker crust (recipe follows)

1. Combine syrup, vanilla and Roma in blender until Roma is dissolved.

2. Add tofu and blend until silky smooth.

3. In a thick-bottom saucepan, melt carob chips.

4. When chips are melted, add to blender and blend, stopping 2 or 3 times to stir contents down. When completely blended, put your blender in the refrigerator while you wait for the graham cracker crust to become completely cool.

5. When crust is cool, spoon in filling and refrigerate. This pie is quite rich and needs to be served very cold. Cut into small pieces.

Serves 12

Nutrients per serving: Calories 249, Protein 4g, Carbohydrate 35g, Fat 12g, Cholesterol 0mg, Saturated Fat 8g, Sodium 69mg, Dietary Fiber 2g

Crunchy
GRAHAM CRACKER CRUST

8 large squares honey-flavored, all-natural graham crackers, crushed into crumbs
3 tablespoons pure maple syrup
2 tablespoons canola oil

1. Mix well.

2. Pat into 9-inch pie plate and bake at 350 degrees F for 12 minutes, or until it begins to brown on edges. Allow to cool completely before adding filling. This crust is very crunchy.

CAROB: A TASTY, HEALTHFUL ALTERNATIVE TO CHOCOLATE

The glossy green leaves and long red or brown pods mark the carob tree (Ceratonia siliqua) as a member of the PULSE family. It is native to the Mediterranean, but can also be grown in other warm climates. The carob tree as a food-producer dates back beyond history. It is thought by many to have been the food eaten by John the Baptist, and is, in fact, sometimes called St. John's bread. It is also known as locust bean gum and is used as a food stabilizer.

Carob pods are filled with a sweet pulp which holds from five to 15 seeds. After a process of sun-drying, the pulp is ground into powder. Carob powder can be used as a substitute for chocolate for people who wish to avoid caffeine and theobromine. Carob powder is commercially blended with other ingredients and formed into carob chips, which make a tasty alternative to chocolate chips.

Carob is a nutritious food, providing high amounts of calcium, phosphorus and potassium, and smaller amounts of sodium and iron. A comparison of some of the properties of carob and chocolate is as follows:

Crude fat:	Carob—0.7 %	Chocolate—23.7 %
Natural sugar:	Carob—47.0 %	Chocolate—5.5 %

Carob also has medicinal qualities, being used in the treatment and prevention of dysentery. It contains pectin and lignin, which regulate digestion and carry harmful elements safely out of the body.

For more information on carob, read an article by C. Nyerges in the December 1978 issue of Organic Gardening, *or go to Encyclopedia.com on the Internet.*

The Best
CAROB FUDGE

Fool a chocoholic! The first time make this recipe with 1 cup chocolate chips and 1 cup carob chips. Next time make it all carob.

2 cups Sunspire carob chips (12 ounces)
1 cup all-natural peanut butter
   (or almond or cashew butter)
1 cup rinsed raisins
1 cup thinly sliced almonds, or coarsely
   chopped pecans
1 cup shredded, unsweetened coconut

1. Melt chips and peanut butter in a heavy-bottom saucepan. (I soak my raisins in hot tap water while the chips melt.)

2. Remove from heat and quickly stir in remaining ingredients. Tends to get thick quickly.

3. Pat out on cookie sheet ⅜ to ½-inch thick. Recipe won't fill cookie sheet.

4. Freeze 20 minutes, and cut into 1-inch squares. Store in reclosable plastic bags in freezer. Serve cold.

Serves 80

Nutrients per serving: Calories 51, Protein 1g, Carbohydrate 4g, Fat 4g, Cholesterol 0mg, Saturated Fat 1g, Sodium 16mg, Dietary Fiber 1g

TIPS FOR COOKING WITH CAROB CHIPS

I use Sunspire vegan chips, which are sometimes difficult to find, or Chatfield's. Barley malt-sweetened chips work too, but your recipe will be sweeter.

Due to the high pectin levels in carob, sometimes the chips won't melt very well. When this happens, I add small amounts of distilled water, ⅛ cup at a time, until the chips melt but are still very thick looking. If you make the chips too thin, your recipe won't set up as well. I don't like using more than ¼ cup water with 3 cups of chips, but I have used as much as ½ cup.

Fudgy Carob
COOKIES OR MINI MUFFINS

½ cup pure maple syrup
½ cup honey
¾ cup applesauce
1½ tablespoons pure vanilla
¾ teaspoon salt
¾ cup carob Rice Dream (nondairy
   beverage)
¼ cup carob powder
1 tablespoon Roma (coffee substitute)
2½ cups quick oats blended into flour in
   dry blender
1½ cups whole-wheat pastry flour
¾ cup thinly sliced almonds
2 to 3 cups carob chips, divided

1. In a bowl beat together syrup, honey, applesauce, vanilla, salt, Rice Dream, carob powder and Roma.

2. Add oat flour, whole-wheat flour, almonds and 1 cup of the carob chips, and mix together well.

3. Let sit for 10 minutes. Drop by 1-tablespoon portions onto sprayed cookie sheet.

4. Sprinkle top of cookies with carob chips. Bake at 350 degrees F for 11 to 12 minutes. Don't overbake. These freeze well.

Serves 69

Nutrients per serving: Calories 83, Protein 2g, Carbohydrate 15g, Fat 2g, Cholesterol 0mg, Saturated Fat 1g, Sodium 30mg, Dietary Fiber 2g

You are today where your thoughts have brought you; you will be tomorrow where your thoughts take you.
—James Allen

HEALTHY DRINKS

SWISS MOCHA ROMA WITH TOFU WHIPPED CREAM

CRANBERRY TEA

HIBISCUS TEA

CAROB "MILK" SHAKE

TROPICAL FROST #2

PEACH JULEP

SEE "DRINKS" IN THE INDEX FOR MANY MORE
DRINK IDEAS THROUGHOUT THE BOOK

*Pictured, clockwise from bottom left: Pumpkin Foamy
(page 112), Swiss Mocha Roma with Tofu Whipped
Cream, Carob "Milk" Shake, Tropical Frost #2,
Hibiscus Tea*

Swiss
MOCHA ROMA

1 tablespoon Roma (coffee substitute)
½ cup water
¾ cup carob Rice Dream (nondairy beverage)
1 tablespoon carob powder
2 tablespoons honey
2 to 3 tablespoons tofu whipped cream (recipe follows; does not need to be refrigerated first)

If anyone thirsts, let him come to Me and drink. He who believes in Me, as the Scripture has said, out of his heart will flow rivers of living water.
—John 7:37-38

1. Combine Roma, water, Rice Dream, carob and honey in blender and blend on medium speed for 30 seconds.

2. Pour into glass 2-cup measuring cup, and heat in microwave for 2 minutes.

3. Pour back into blender and blend in the tofu whipped cream. Serve immediately. Makes 1½ cups.

Serves 2

Nutrients per serving: Calories 178, Protein 2g, Carbohydrate 38g, Fat 2.5g, Cholesterol 0mg, Saturated Fat 0g, Sodium 75mg, Dietary Fiber 1g

Tofu
WHIPPED CREAM

This keeps well in the refrigerator for 5 to 6 days. Try it with fresh or frozen fruit to make a fruited cream, or layer with granola (page 98) to make a great parfait!

1 cup firm, silken Lite Mori-Nu tofu
½ teaspoon lemon juice
1 tablespoon plus 1½ teaspoons canola oil
⅛ teaspoon salt
2 teaspoons water
1½ teaspoons pure vanilla
2 tablespoons honey

In a blender blend all ingredients until smooth. Refrigerate for 2 hours to give the whipped cream a rich flavor.

Cranberry
TEA

1 bag fresh cranberries, or 1⅛ cup unsweetened pure cranberry juice
3 cinnamon sticks
Juice from one orange
Juice from one lemon
5 whole cloves
½ cup honey
1½ quarts water and 1½ cups water after cooking

1. In a large Dutch oven, combine cranberries (or juice), cinnamon sticks, juices, cloves, honey and 1½ quarts water. Simmer 45 to 60 minutes.

2. Add remaining water. Strain out berries if used. Serve with a cinnamon stick in each glass. Great holiday tea!

Serves 12

Nutrients per serving: Calories 62, Protein 0g, Carbohydrate 16g, Fat 0g, Cholesterol 0mg, Saturated Fat 0g, Sodium 6mg, Dietary Fiber 0g

Hibiscus
TEA

This easily replaces sweetened tea. It's not only a beautiful color; it smells and tastes fantastic. I make a gallon at a time. See my resources section (page 128) to purchase tea from Mrs. Mango & Co.

2 quarts water
8 hibiscus flower tea bags
½ cup honey

1. Bring water to a boil and add tea bags.

2. Steep for 30 minutes. Remove bags and let cool.

3. Add honey. Refrigerate and serve cold.

Serves 8

Nutrients per serving: Calories 43, Protein 0g, Carbohydrate 11g, Fat 0g, Cholesterol 0mg, Saturated Fat 0g, Sodium 8mg, Dietary Fiber 0g

Carob
"MILK" SHAKE

Children love this shake; we make this recipe almost every day during the summer months.

1½ frozen bananas
1 tablespoon carob powder
2 tablespoons pure maple syrup
1 teaspoon pure vanilla
1 cup carob Rice Dream (nondairy beverage)
6 ice cubes

1. Blend everything except ice cubes until smooth, stopping blender once or twice to stir.

2. Add ice cubes and blend well. Serve immediately.

Makes 2 twelve-ounce servings

Nutrients per serving: Calories 213, Protein 2g, Carbohydrate 55g, Fat 2g, Cholesterol 0mg, Saturated Fat 0g, Sodium 56mg, Dietary Fiber 2g

Tropical
FROST #2

½ cup coconut juice, Lakewood brand
1 tablespoon pure lime juice concentrate
1 frozen banana
1 tablespoon shredded, unsweetened coconut
4 to 6 ice cubes

1. Blend everything except ice cubes until smooth.

2. Add ice cubes and blend again.

Makes 4 five-ounce servings

Nutrients per serving: Calories 70, Protein 5g, Carbohydrate 15g, Fat 1g, Cholesterol 0mg, Saturated Fat 1g, Sodium 3mg, Dietary Fiber 1g

Peach
JULEP

8 cups coarsely crushed ice
3 cups fresh peach juice or peach nectar
1 cup pink grapefruit juice, freshly squeezed (see warning note)

1. Crush ice in food processor; place in glasses.

2. Mix juices and pour over the ice.

3. Garnish each glass with a sprig of mint and serve immediately.

Beware: Some store-bought pink grapefruit juices contain carmine and/or cochineal extract. This is a red pigment extracted from a bright red South American female scale insect. Contact these companies and ask them to remove these offending ingredients. Read your labels!

Makes 12 one-cup servings

Nutrients per serving: Calories 42, Protein <1g, Carbohydrate 10g, Fat 0g, Cholesterol 0mg, Saturated Fat 0g, Sodium 5mg, Dietary Fiber 0g

It's a funny thing about life; if you refuse to accept anything but the best, you very often get it.
—W. Somerset Maugham

MAKING DRINKS FROM PURE WATER

I always make my ice cubes with pure, distilled water so they're ready to mix into healthful drinks.

TIP FOR KEEPING FROZEN BANANAS

As your bananas ripen on your counter, peel, put in reclosable plastic bags, remove the air and freeze. They won't turn brown if you get the air out of the plastic bag, and you'll always have frozen bananas ready for drinks. (Some brand-name bags tend to leak air, so I use generic.)

POTPOURRI

A ROMANIAN MEAL
CABBAGE ROLLS
DILL POTATOES
DILL SALAD
SUPÂ DE LEGUMÂ
COOKED CABBAGE
ROMANIAN EGGPLANT SPREAD
RECIPE IN HOME FOR THE HOLIDAYS SECTION

COOKING WITH GARLIC
DELIGHTFUL DILL SPREAD, FRENCH DRESSING, GARLIC POTATOES, PLUM TOMATO SAUCE

COOKING WITH CARROTS
VEGGIE TUNA, CARROT PALM TREE GARNISH, CARROT MACAROONS

DRESSINGS
OIL & LEMON DRESSING, NEW LIFE SALAD DRESSING, AVOCADO CREAM BREAD SPREAD

Cabbage Rolls

¼ cup canola oil
2 large carrots, shredded
1 large parsnip, shredded
1½ large onions, chopped
1½ cups mushrooms, chopped
1 teaspoon paprika
1 tablespoon McKay's chicken-style
   or Bill's Best Chik Nish seasoning
   (if using Bill's Best, increase salt by
   ½ teaspoon)
2 teaspoons salt
½ cup fresh dill, chopped and lightly
   packed into cup
⅓ cup whole-wheat pastry flour
½ cup farina or dry Cream of Wheat
   cereal
6 cups cooked brown rice
   (recipe follows)
Juice of one lemon
2 heads cabbage, core removed
4 whole green onions

SAUCE:
3 or 4 large tomatoes
⅓ cup canola oil
¾ teaspoon salt

1. Put oil, carrots, parsnip, onion, mushrooms, paprika, seasoning and salt in a large pan and cook until soft, but not brown. Add dill, flour, farina and cooked brown rice. Mix well to form a thick paste; set aside.

2. To prepare cabbage: Fill two large Dutch ovens halfway with water, and bring to a boil. Put the lemon juice in one pan and remove from heat.

3. In the plain water, put one head of cabbage. In a few minutes you will be able to remove the outer leaves with tongs. Place removed leaves in the lemon water and allow to soak for about 10 minutes.

4. Remove leaves to a towel-lined cooling rack to drain. Depending on the size of your cabbage leaves, use either a ⅛ cup measuring cup or ¼ cup measure for the filling. Scoop filling onto the bottom edge of the cabbage leaf and roll just until filling is covered. Tuck in left and right sides and continue to roll up. Repeat with remaining cabbage leaves.

5. In a large Dutch oven, form a grid using the four green onions. Set the finished cabbage rolls in a circular fashion filling up the bottom of the pan. Continue to stack on top of each other.

6. In a blender, blend the tomatoes, oil and salt until mostly smooth. Pour over the cabbage rolls, cover and bring to a boil. Cook on low for about 30 minutes. These can also be baked in the oven at 350 degrees F for 45 minutes.

BROWN RICE:
2 cups brown rice
1 tablespoon oil
4 cups water
¾ teaspoon salt

Bring above to a boil. Cover and simmer on low about 45 minutes or until water is absorbed and rice is tender. Do not stir rice while it is cooking. Stirring activates the gluten and causes the rice to become extra sticky. This recipe makes a little more than what you need for the cabbage rolls.

Makes 40 medium servings

Nutrients per serving: Calories 86, Protein 2g, Carbohydrate 12g, Fat 4g, Cholesterol trace, Saturated Fat 0g, Sodium 275mg, Dietary Fiber 1g

Dill POTATOES

¼ cup canola oil
2½ cups water
1 teaspoon salt
4 cloves garlic, crushed
2 tablespoons vegetable bouillon and
 seasoning
¾ cup fresh dill, chopped
½ to 3 pounds potatoes, scrubbed and cut
 into ½-inch cubes

1. Combine all in a large bowl.

2. Pour into a 9 x 13-inch baking dish. Bake covered at 350 degrees F for 30 minutes.

3. Remove cover and bake until water evaporates, about 20 minutes longer. Add more salt if needed and serve.

Serves 8

Nutrients per serving: Calories 12, Protein 0g, Carbohydrate 2g, Fat 1g, Cholesterol 0mg, Saturated Fat 0g, Sodium 23mg, Dietary Fiber 0g

Supâ DE LEGUMÂ

1 large onion, chopped
2 carrots, shredded
⅓ cup parsnip or turnip greens, chopped
 and packed into cup
3 potatoes, thinly sliced
1 tablespoon canola oil
3½ quarts water
⅓ cup fresh parsley, chopped and packed
 into cup

Bring everything but parsley to a boil. Boil 30 minutes or until potatoes begin to fall apart. Remove from heat and stir in parsley. Serve hot.

Serves 16

Nutrients per serving: Calories 38, Protein 1g, Carbohydrate 7g, Fat 1g, Cholesterol 0mg, Saturated Fat 0g, Sodium 12mg, Dietary Fiber 1g

The love we give away is the only love we keep.
—Elbert Hubbard

Dill SALAD

4 cups cucumbers, sliced thin
4 cups tomato wedges
½ cup green onion, chopped (green part)
1½ tablespoon fresh dill, chopped
Squeeze of lemon
Salt

Toss all together, salting to taste. Chill 2 hours for flavors to blend.

Serves 16

Nutrients per serving: Calories 10, Protein 0g, Carbohydrate 2g, Fat 0g, Cholesterol 0mg, Saturated Fat 0g, Sodium 3mg, Dietary Fiber 1g

COOKING ROMANIAN-STYLE

In May 1999 I spent a month in Romania sharing cooking and health information with 1,000 people every night. I learned from them too! I wish I had had more time in Romania learning how to cook their delicacies. Their food is simple but delicious. My thanks to Debora Calotá and Ester Palhegi for help with my Romanian recipes.

Cooked CABBAGE

The most wasted day of all is that on which we have not laughed.
—Chamfort

2 large onions, chopped
⅛ cup extra-virgin olive oil
½ cup water
1 head cabbage, diced
1 green onion, both parts, diced
½ cup parsnip or turnip greens, chopped
¼ cup fresh-chopped dill, lightly packed into cup
2 medium to large tomatoes, diced
2 large cloves garlic, minced
1½ teaspoon salt

1. In a large Dutch oven, cook onion in oil and water until soft.

2. Add cabbage, green onion, parsnip or turnip greens, dill and tomatoes. Simmer uncovered about 45 minutes allowing about ¾ of the water to evaporate.

3. When done, stir in garlic, adjust salt if necessary, and serve hot. The consistency should be thick, not soupy. Delicious!

Serves 20

Nutrients per serving: Calories 27, Protein 1g, Carbohydrate 3g, Fat 2g, Cholesterol 0mg, Saturated Fat 0g, Sodium 168mg, Dietary Fiber 1g

Delightful DILL SPREAD

This spread can also be used on baked potatoes or as a dip for veggies.

1 box (12.3 ounces) silken, extra-firm Mori Nu tofu
½ cup Vegenaise
1½ teaspoons dill weed
½ teaspoon onion powder
½ teaspoon salt
1 teaspoon dried minced onions
1 teaspoon honey

In a medium-sized food processor, process to smooth. Refrigerate for flavors to blend.

Makes 32 one-tablespoon servings

Nutrients per serving: Calories 39, Protein 1.5g, Carbohydrate 1g, Fat 3g, Cholesterol 0mg, Saturated Fat 0g, Sodium 55mg, Dietary Fiber 0g

French DRESSING

This is my favorite dressing recipe. The more tomato you add, the thicker it gets. This is wonderful as a dip for raw veggies, but make it thicker to use as dip.

⅜ cup (¼ + ⅛) canola oil
½ teaspoon paprika
⅓ cup raw honey
¼ cup onion
½ teaspoon salt, or to taste
1 large clove garlic
¼ cup fresh lemon juice
2 cups cubed, vine-ripened tomatoes

Blend ingredients until smooth. Can be stored in refrigerator 7 to 10 days.

Makes 24 one-ounce servings

Nutrients per serving: Calories 47, Protein 0g, Carbohydrate 4g, Fat 3g, Cholesterol 0mg, Saturated Fat 0g, Sodium 47mg, Dietary Fiber 0g

Plum
TOMATO SAUCE

This recipe was created by my dear friend Claudia Welty. I recommend this sauce with DeBole's tomato and parsley fettuccine noodles or angel hair pasta. This is also the perfect topping for Claudia's garlic potatoes (recipe at right).

2 tablespoon olive oil
10 cloves garlic sliced or chopped
1 medium sweet onion chopped
1 large red or yellow pepper, sliced and
   cut into small squares
½ can (about 1 cup) black olives sliced or
   chopped
6 large plum tomatoes, diced
1 teaspoon dried or fresh thyme
1 teaspoon salt

1. Heat olive oil in a nonstick skillet. Add garlic and cook until golden.

2. Add remaining ingredients, stir together and cook on low for 15 to 20 minutes.

Serves 8

Nutrients per serving: Calories 75, Protein 1g, Carbohydrate 7g, Fat 5g, Cholesterol 0mg, Saturated Fat 1g, Sodium 323mg, Dietary Fiber 2g

Garlic
POTATOES

Add a dollop of dill spread and plum tomato sauce (recipes at left). Be creative!

4 large baking potatoes
15 to 20 cloves of garlic
4 teaspoon olive oil
Liquid aminos

1. Wash potatoes and slice in half lengthwise.

2. With a spoon, scoop out middle leaving ½ inch on the sides and bottom. Discard centers or bake in a separate dish.

3. Place 4 to 5 garlic cloves, and 1 teaspoon olive oil inside each potato. Use 4 toothpicks to secure halves together.

4. Microwave approximately 8 minutes, turning once at 4 minutes, or bake at 350 degrees F for 50 to 60 minutes. After baking, squirt liquid aminos on potato instead of adding salt, and add a dollop of plum tomato sauce. Delicious!

Serves 8

Nutrients per serving: Calories 256, Protein 6g, Carbohydrate 55g, Fat 4g, Cholesterol 0mg, Saturated Fat .5g, Sodium 0mg, Dietary Fiber 5g

The only way to have a friend is to be one.
—Ralph Waldo Emerson

THE BENEFITS OF GARLIC

Besides adding "zip" to your cooking, there is some evidence that garlic may be beneficial in preventing AIDS, cancer, heart disease, stroke, diabetes, lead poisoning, herpes and other viral infections. Raw garlic is much more advantageous than commercially available garlic pills. If one or two cloves are diced small, they can be quickly swallowed with water and will leave no odor. A sprig of fresh parsley may be chewed to eliminate all possibility of offensive breath.

NIGHTSHADE FAMILY VEGETABLES

According to Prescription for Cooking and Dietary Wellness by James and Phyllis Balch, elimination of night-shade vegetables from the diet may be helpful if one suffers from arthritis, bone loss, or aching joints and muscles. Vegetables of the nightshade family include bell peppers of all colors, cayenne pepper (capsicum), chili peppers, eggplant, hot peppers, paprika, pimento, potatoes and tomatoes.

For more information, please read *Prescription for Cooking and Dietary Wellness*, by Phyllis A. Balch, CNC, and James F. Balch, M.D.

Veggie Tuna

I use this as a sandwich filling or serve it on crackers. I've even hollowed out cucumbers and filled them with this mixture.

2 cups carrots, shredded and finely chopped
2 stalks celery, diced very small
1 bell pepper, diced small
¼ cup red onion, diced very small
1 tomato, cut into small squares
1 tablespoon liquid aminos
⅓ cup Vegenaise
Salt

1. If using a food processor to cut up vegetables, be careful not to turn them into mush. Drain off any liquid from tomatoes or other veggies.

2. Combine all, adjusting mayonnaise and salt to taste.

Makes 20 quarter-cup servings

Nutrients per serving: Calories 45, Protein 0g, Carbohydrate 3g, Fat 4g, Cholesterol 0mg, Saturated Fat trace, Sodium 75mg, Dietary Fiber 1g

RETRAIN YOUR TASTE BUDS

When tasting a new food for the first time, you must take two bites. The first bite retrains the taste buds; the second will actually give you the truer taste.

Carrot
PALM TREE GARNISH

1 large, oval potato
1 large, thick carrot
1 green pepper with three lobes
5-inch utility knife
Paring knife
Vegetable peeler
V-shaped cutter
Toothpick

1. Make a base by using the 5-inch knife to cut a slice from the long side of the potato so it will sit flat.

2. Using the paring knife, trace the bottom of the carrot onto the middle of the potato, and using a spoon, hollow out a space for the carrot to fit down into the potato. Make sure not to cut the hole too large.

3. Peel the carrot with the vegetable peeler. Cut off the top and tip.

4. Starting at the thick end of the carrot, use the paring knife to make a series of ½-inch long upside-down v-shaped cuts going all the way around. Make a second row just above this one, cutting so that the v shape is between the two v's below. Continue making these cuts until you reach the narrow end of the carrot. Press the carrot into the base.

5. Press the v-shaped cutter into the green pepper about ¾ inch from the stem end. Make another cut beside it so that it joins the first v. Continue to cut all around the pepper. Remove insides and rinse well.

6. Break a toothpick in half and insert the dull end into the top of the carrot, then press the pepper onto the carrot.

Your "palm trees" can be made a day ahead by soaking all the finished vegetable parts in ice water.

Carrot MACAROONS

My personal favorite health cookie!

1 cup grated raw carrots (about
    2 medium to large) packed into
    measuring cup
½ cup water, or enough to pour over
    carrots to fill cup
½ cup honey
⅛ cup canola oil
1 teaspoon vanilla
2 cups shredded, unsweetened coconut
½ cup whole-wheat pastry flour
½ teaspoon salt

1. Mix above ingredients well. Let sit for 5 to 10 minutes.

2. Measure out 1-tablespoon cookies and pat each one slightly flat and round.

3. Bake at 350 degrees F for 20 to 25 minutes or until edges turn a medium brown. These cookies are better a little crispier.

Serves 65

Nutrients per serving: Calories 12, Protein 0g, Carbohydrate 2g, Fat .5g, Cholesterol 0mg, Saturated Fat 0g, Sodium 8mg, Dietary Fiber trace

Oil & LEMON DRESSING

1 part lemon juice
2 parts extra-virgin olive oil
Salt

Combine juice and oil; salt to taste. A little of this dressing goes a long way; use sparingly. Shake ingredients together in a closed container before each use.

Makes 12 one-tablespoon servings

Nutrients per serving: Calories 82, Protein 0g, Carbohydrate 0g, Fat 8g, Cholesterol 0mg, Saturated Fat 1g, Sodium 89mg, Dietary Fiber 0g

New Life SALAD DRESSING

½ cup water
½ cup extra-virgin olive oil
¼ cup fresh lemon juice
½ cup onion, packed into cup
1 medium clove garlic
⅛ cup honey
¼ teaspoon salt

Blend all to smooth and creamy. Can be stored in refrigerator for 4 to 5 days.

Makes 16 one-ounce servings

Nutrients per serving: Calories 71, Protein 0g, Carbohydrate 3g, Fat 7g, Cholesterol 0mg, Saturated Fat trace, Sodium 34mg, Dietary Fiber 0g

Avocado Cream BREAD SPREAD

1 large ripe avocado
1 box (12.3 ounces) silken, firm tofu
¼ cup fresh lemon juice
½ teaspoon salt
⅛ cup honey
⅛ cup onion, packed into cup
1 small clove garlic

1. Cut avocado in half. Remove seed and scoop out pulp.

2. Blend avocado with other ingredients until smooth and creamy.

3. Chill. Keeps 3 days. Serve on toast or as a thick dressing.

Makes 23 one-ounce servings

Nutrients per serving: Calories 26, Protein 1g, Carbohydrate 3g, Fat 1g, Cholesterol 0mg, Saturated Fat 0g, Sodium 57mg, Dietary Fiber 0g

If you know these things, happy are you if you do them.
—John 13:17

Bread Delicacies & Great Grains

Basic Whole-Wheat Bread Machine Loaf

Whole-Wheat Flax Bread

Sprouted Wheat Bread

Rustic Roma Tomato & Pesto Pizza

Apricot-Carob Chip Tea Ring

Communion Bread

Cooking with Oats:
Quick & Easy Granola, Oat Pizza Crust with Vegan Parmesan Cheese

Quinoa, Supergrain of the Future:
Basic Quinoa Recipe, Hot Nutty Quinoa, Quinoa Corn Bread, Quinoa Stir-Fry

Pictured, bottom to top: Apricot-Carob Chip Tea Ring,
Rustic Roma Tomato & Pesto Pizza, Whole-Wheat Flax
Bread

Basic WHOLE-WHEAT BREAD MACHINE LOAF

1 tablespoon yeast
2 cups whole-wheat bread flour
3 cups whole-wheat pastry flour
2½ teaspoon salt
¼ cup lecithin granules
⅜ cup (¼ + ⅛) wheat germ
½ cup honey
¼ cup extra-virgin olive oil
1¼ cups warm water

Add ingredients in order listed, placing yeast in one corner. I set my machine on the rapid whole-wheat setting. I also remove my bread 6 to 10 minutes early so it doesn't overbrown. My machine always seems to overbake it a little.

Makes one 2-pound loaf; serves 25

Nutrients per serving: Calories 128, Protein 4g, Carbohydrate 24g, Fat 3g, Cholesterol 0mg, Saturated Fat trace, Sodium 215mg, Dietary Fiber 3g

And Jesus said unto them, "I am the bread of life: he that cometh to Me shall never hunger; and he that believeth on Me shall never thirst."
—John 6:35

MEASURING FLOUR

When using any type of flour in a recipe, always "fluff" the flour with your hands, then spoon it into your measuring cup and level off with a knife. Using the measuring cup to scoop out flour can add as much as 2 additional tablespoons to the recipe, making your dough tough and dry.

Whole-Wheat FLAX BREAD

1 tablespoon dry yeast
1¾ cups warm water
⅛ cup honey
2 cups whole-wheat pastry flour, divided
2 cups whole-wheat bread flour, divided
2 teaspoons salt
2 tablespoons extra-virgin olive oil
¼ cup flax seeds
Additional ½ cup to 1 cup whole-wheat pastry flour

1. Dissolve yeast in warm honey water. Wait 10 minutes. A thick foam will form on the top of your water indicating that the yeast is alive.

2. In a large mixing bowl put 2 cups of the flour, oil and salt; mix well. Pour in yeast mixture. Stir for 5 minutes until gluten has formed. (Flour becomes very elastic. This is a critical step in your bread's turning out.)

3. Add the last 2 cups of flour and flax seeds. If you have a mixer with dough hooks, you can let it knead the dough for you for the next 10 minutes. Otherwise, knead by hand, adding enough flour to keep it from being too sticky.

4. Rub a little oil over the top of your dough and cover with plastic wrap and a small hand towel. Place in a warm place and allow to double in size, about 1 hour.

5. Punch down and shape into 2 medium loaves or 1 large loaf. Allow to rise once more in oiled loaf pan(s). Bake at 350 degrees F for 45 to 50 minutes.

Makes one 2-pound loaf; serves 25

Nutrients per serving: Calories 105, Protein 4g, Carbohydrate 19g, Fat 2g, Cholesterol 0mg, Saturated Fat trace, Sodium 173mg, Dietary Fiber 3g

Sprouted
Wheat Bread

This is Susan Grimm's recipe. See my resources section (page 128) for more about Susan and Harvest-Time Foods.

½ cup wheat sprout flour
   (instructions follow)
1 tablespoon active dry yeast
½ cup warm water
3½ cups fresh-ground
   hard red wheat flour
2½ teaspoon salt
1 tablespoon lecithin granules
⅛ cup high-gluten
   unbleached white flour
1 teaspoon vitamin C granules
2¼ cups warm water
½ cup chopped wheat sprouts
   (see step 3 at right)
Additional 1½ to 3 cups gluten flour

To make wheat sprout flour:

1. Soak 1 cup of wheat berries in warm water for 8 hours. Rinse with clean water and drain. Lay out evenly in a flat dish and cover with a damp dish towel.

2. Place in a cool dark place (refrigerator is too cold, pantry is okay). For 48 hours, or until sprouts are ¼-inch long, put into a colander twice a day and rinse with clean water. Quarter-inch sprouts are at their peak of sweetness.

3. Put on trays to dry out or you can use your commercial dehydrator or convection oven set on air only. Dehydrate until they are completely hard again and grind into flour.

To make the bread:

1. Mix wheat sprout flour, yeast and warm water together and set aside.

2. In a separate bowl mix together hard red wheat flour, salt, lecithin, ⅛ cup of the gluten flour, vitamin C, warm water and chopped wheat sprouts.

3. To make chopped wheat sprouts, follow the same procedure for wheat sprout flour, only when the sprouts are ¼-inch long, freeze them in ½-cup portions. Do not dehydrate. Remove from freezer when ready to use and pulse in food processor.

4. Combine yeast mixture with flour mixture and mix well (300 strokes).

5. Add an additional 1½ cups to 3 cups gluten flour. Knead well and shape into two loaves. Allow to rise, and bake for 35 minutes at 350 degrees F.

Serves 25

Nutrients per serving: Calories 112, Protein 4g, Carbohydrate 23g, Fat 1g, Cholesterol 0mg, Saturated Fat trace, Sodium 216mg, Dietary Fiber 3g

Always do more than is required of you.
—George S. Patton

Rustic
ROMA TOMATO & PESTO PIZZA

WHOLE-WHEAT CRUST:
3½ cups to 4 cups whole-wheat pastry
   flour
¾ cup fine corn meal
4 teaspoons or 2 packages quick-rising
   yeast
2 teaspoons salt
2 tablespoons sucanat
⅜ cup (¼ + ⅛) extra-virgin olive oil
1 cup warm water (between 110 degrees F
   and 120 degrees F)

PESTO SAUCE:
½ cup extra-virgin olive oil
1 cup fresh basil, packed into cup
½ cup pine nuts
¾ teaspoon salt

TOPPING:
1 medium to large yellow summer
   squash, sliced into thin rounds
4 to 5 roma tomatoes, sliced into thin
   rounds
Fresh sprigs of thyme for garnish
Salt

To make the crust:

1. In a large food processor combine the dry
ingredients, and pulse to mix.

2. Add the water and oil through the spout and
form dough. Knead for one minute. You don't
want the dough too sticky or dry. Adjust flour or
water if necessary.

3. Remove from food processor; rub a little oil
over dough and cover with plastic wrap and a
dish towel. Allow to rise in a warm place for
20 to 30 minutes.

To make the pesto:

In a food processor or blender process all the
ingredients until smooth; set aside.

To assemble:

1. Roll out dough on an oiled 15-inch pizza pan
⅜-inch thick, extending dough 2 to 3 inches
larger than the pan in all directions.

2. Spread out pesto sauce evenly on dough just
to the edge of the pizza pan, not beyond. In a
circular fashion, alternate summer squash with
tomato rounds, slightly overlapping each other,
covering entire pesto area. Cut a few sprigs of
thyme over tomatoes and lightly sprinkle pizza
with salt.

3. Fold dough overhang over the top of the pizza
and pleat the dough every inch or so. You will
have about a 10-inch circle in the center where
you can see the filling. Bake at 425 degrees F for
30 to 35 minutes until bubbly and browning.

Serves 12

*Nutrients per serving: Calories 369, Protein 9g,
Carbohydrate 44g, Fat 22g, Cholesterol 0mg,
Saturated Fat 3g, Sodium 500mg, Dietary Fiber 8g*

Apricot- CAROB CHIP TEA RING

DOUGH:
2½ teaspoons quick-rising yeast
1 cup plus 2 tablespoons warm water
¼ cup sucanat, divided
3½ cups whole-wheat pastry flour
1 teaspoon salt
1 tablespoon canola oil

FILLING:
1 jar (15 ounces, or 2 cups) apricot
  all-fruit jam
½ cup dried apricots, diced into small
  pieces
½ cup carob chips

ICING:
1 cup carob chips
½ cup apricot all-fruit jam
¼ cup Hokan Lite coconut milk

To make the dough:

1. Dissolve the yeast into warm water with
1 tablespoon of the sucanat. Wait 10 minutes
until yeast mixture is bubbly.

2. In a mixing bowl, mix together 2 cups of the
whole-wheat pastry flour, remaining sucanat and
salt. Stir in yeast mixture and oil. Knead with
dough hooks for 5 minutes to form the
gluten. (This dough can also be made in a food
processor.)

3. Add remaining flour and knead another 3 to 4
minutes. Dough should not be sticky.

To assemble:

1. Lightly flour a work surface and roll out
dough into a 20 x 15-inch rectangle. Cut side
edges straight. Spread jam evenly leaving 1 inch
along bottom sealing edge. Sprinkle with apricots and carob chips.

2. Carefully roll up, forming a long tube. Gently
lift dough onto a 15-inch round baking stone
or pan. Shape into a circle, sealing ends. With
scissors, cutting from the outer edge to the
inside, cut ¾-inch slices to within ½ inch of the
inside of the ring. Carefully turn each slice on its
side. Allow to rise in a warm place, covered, for
20 to 25 minutes. Bake at 325 degrees F for 35 to
40 minutes or until bubbly and browning. Cool
before icing.

To make the icing:

Melt together carob chips, jam and coconut
milk. Generously drizzle over tea ring and serve.

Serves 20

*Nutrients per serving: Calories 295, Protein 5g,
Carbohydrate 56g, Fat 7g, Cholesterol 0mg,
Saturated Fat 2g, Sodium 113mg, Dietary Fiber 3g*

*No matter where
you go, there you are.
—Unknown*

Communion
BREAD

In the summer of 1999, I visited the Norwalk, California, Seventh-day Adventist church. During their communion service, they served big, thick pieces of communion bread that were absolutely delicious. This is a slight adaptation of their recipe.

5 cups whole-wheat pastry flour
1¼ teaspoons salt
½ cup canola oil
¼ cup extra-virgin olive oil
¾ cup water

Whatever you can do or dream you can, begin it.
—Goethe

1. Using a spoon, fill measuring cup with flour and level off with a knife.

2. Mix flour and salt together.

3. Add oils, and mix to form crumbs.

4. Add water, and knead for 1 minute. Dough will be thick.

5. Roll out ⅜-inch thick. Using a pizza cutter, cut into 1-inch squares. Leave ½-inch spaces between pieces; bake at 350 degrees F for 30 to 35 minutes.

Serves 40

Nutrients per serving: Calories 87, Protein 2g, Carbohydrate 11g, Fat 4g, Cholesterol 0mg, Saturated Fat trace, Sodium 68mg, Dietary Fiber 2g

Quick & Easy
GRANOLA

Thirty-five minutes, start to finish!

½ cup pure maple syrup
½ cup canola oil
½ cup honey
1½ teaspoons salt
1 tablespoon pure vanilla
8 cups regular oats

1. Whisk together everything except oats.

2. Pour over oats in large bowl; stir until well coated.

3. Put oats into glass 10 x 14-inch baking dish and bake at 350 degrees F for 20 minutes. Stir, then bake for another 10 minutes. Should begin to dry out, and oats will start to change color.

A glass baking dish makes it easier to watch for the color change. If you bake in a 9 x 13-inch pan, you will need to increase your baking time by 10 minutes.

Variations:

Add 1 cup raisins or favorite dried fruit to cool granola (children tend to like just plain oats the best).

Maple-pecan granola: Use 1 cup maple syrup and no honey. Bake for 20 minutes, stir, and sprinkle with 1 cup chopped pecans. Return to oven for remaining 10 minutes. Mix and store.

Honey-almond granola: Use 1 cup honey and no maple syrup. Bake for 20 minutes, stir, and sprinkle with 1 cup sliced almonds. Return to oven for 10 minutes. Mix and store.

Makes 20 half-cup servings

Nutrients per serving: Calories 340, Protein 11g, Carbohydrate 54g, Fat 10g, Cholesterol 0mg, Saturated Fat 1g, Sodium 162mg, Dietary Fiber 8g

Oat
PIZZA CRUST

2¼ cups whole-wheat pastry flour
1½ cup quick oats
2 tablespoons honey
2 teaspoons onion powder
2 teaspoons dill weed (optional)
¾ teaspoon salt
1 tablespoon canola
1 cup distilled water

1. Mix together everything but the flour. When making crust for children, I omit the dill weed.

2. Mix in the water until no dry flour remains.

3. Knead by hand for 1 minute without using any extra flour on your counter.

4. Shape into circle, lightly flour pizza pan surface and roll out to edges. This dough does not rise.

For a chewier crust, roll out this recipe on a 13-inch pan, and for a crispier, thinner crust roll out recipe on a 15-inch pizza pan.

Topping the pizza:

I top my pizza with a generous amount of Five Brother's tomato sauce (it is low in fat and dairy-free). Then add your favorite toppings:

Onion rings
Green pepper rings
Olives
Mushrooms
Steamed broccoli
Whatever you like

Bake at 350 degrees F for 35 to 45 minutes. Add vegan parmesan "cheese" last 10 minutes of baking.

Serves 20

Nutrients per serving (crust only): Calories 105, Protein 4g, Carbohydrate 19g, Fat 2g, Cholesterol 0mg, Saturated Fat trace, Sodium 82mg, Dietary Fiber 3g

Vegan
PARMESAN "CHEESE"

½ cup sesame seeds
¼ cup nutritional yeast flakes
  (brewer's yeast)
2 teaspoons garlic powder
1 teaspoon onion powder
2 teaspoons McKay's chicken- or beef-
  style seasoning
3 teaspoons lemon juice

1. Grind sesame seeds in blender or food grinder. Takes about 10 minutes in blender.

2. Add remaining ingredients. Pulse in blender until coarse-looking. Store in airtight container. Sprinkle on pizzas or salads, wherever you would use parmesan cheese. Freezes well.

Makes 12 one-tablespoon servings

Nutrients per serving: Calories 43, Protein 2g, Carbohydrate 3g, Fat 3g, Cholesterol 0mg, Saturated Fat trace, Sodium 79mg, Dietary Fiber 1g

MORE ALTERNATIVES TO CHEESE

Galaxy Foods has created a line of cheese alternatives that taste excellent. Their products are tofu-based, but do contain casseinate, a milk protein. Their parmesan-style cheese, Veggie Shreds and American-flavor Veggie Slices are my favorites.

Keep your face to the sunshine and you cannot see the shadow.
—Helen Keller

Basic QUINOA RECIPE

Use in pancakes, waffles, muffins, breads, stews, stir-fries, pilafs, salads, soup and any dish in which you would put rice. Add any combination of steamed vegetables for a great side dish.

2 cups distilled water
½ teaspoon salt
1 cup rinsed quinoa

1. Bring water and salt to a boil; add quinoa.

2. Cover and simmer on low for 17 to 19 minutes.

3. Let sit covered for 5 minutes before serving.

Serves 6

Nutrients per serving: Calories 106, Protein 4g, Carbohydrate 20g, Fat 2g, Cholesterol 0mg, Saturated Fat trace, Sodium 186mg, Dietary Fiber 2g

Hot NUTTY QUINOA

2 cups distilled water
1 cup rinsed quinoa
⅜ cup (¼ + ⅛) pure maple syrup
¼ cup unsweetened shredded coconut
1 teaspoon cinnamon
½ cup coarsely chopped almonds
Milk substitute

1. Bring water to a boil and add other ingredients.

2. Simmer covered on low for 20 minutes. Quinoa will be transparent.

3. To serve, add ½ to ¾ cup almond milk or soy beverage. Substitute any ingredient for your favorite.

Serves 8

Nutrients per serving: Calories 181, Protein 5g, Carbohydrate 27g, Fat 7g, Cholesterol 0mg, Saturated Fat 1g, Sodium 10mg, Dietary Fiber 2g

QUINOA, SUPERGRAIN OF THE FUTURE

Quinoa (pronounced keen-wa), is a tiny seed grown in the Andes mountains of South America. This grain is so important to the Incas that it is considered their mother grain, and with corn and potatoes makes up their staple diet. Legend tells us that in ancient times, the Inca king used a solid gold shovel to plant the first row of quinoa each year.

Quinoa contains more protein than any other grain.

Quinoa	**16.2 % (average; some varieties are over 20%)**
Rice	**7.5 %**
Millet	**9.9 %**
Wheat	**14.0 %**

This grain contains an essential amino acid balance which makes it a complete protein, high in lysine, methionine and cystine. Other grains are low in lysine, and soy is low in methionine and cystine. Quinoa also provides, starch, sugars, oil (which is high in essential linoleic acid), fiber, minerals and vitamins.

One of the most beneficial traits of quinoa is that it is an extremely light grain, which makes it easy to digest. Grinding the seeds into flour provides a wheat-free base from which to make baked goods. The grain itself is so versatile that it can be eaten as a cereal or added to soup, salad or desserts.

Quinoa
CORN BREAD

1 medium sweet onion, chopped fine
1 tablespoon liquid aminos
2 cups high-lysine cornmeal
1 cup quinoa flour (grind quinoa in a dry
    blender about 5 minutes)
2 teaspoon salt
1½ teaspoons Rumford's aluminum-free
    baking powder
½ teaspoon baking soda
1 teaspoon garlic salt
2 teaspoons onion powder
⅓ cup natural applesauce
1¾ cup almond milk
2 tablespoons honey

1. Cook onion and liquid aminos in a skillet until brown.

2. Combine dry ingredients in a bowl.

3. In a separate bowl combine wet ingredients, whisk together and pour over dry ingredients. Add onion and mix well.

4. Pour into oil-sprayed 9 x 9-inch pan and bake at 425 degrees F for 25 to 30 minutes. Serve hot with a little pure maple syrup drizzled over.

Serves 12

Nutrients per serving: Calories 159, Protein 4g, Carbohydrate 33g, Fat 2g, Cholesterol 0mg, Saturated Fat trace, Sodium 682mg, Dietary Fiber 4g

Quinoa
STIR-FRY

Not only tastes great, but is beautiful to the eye!

1 large sweet onion, cut into 1-inch strips
2 stalks celery, cut diagonally into
    ½-inch pieces
1 small zucchini, peeled and sliced thin
1 medium yellow summer squash, sliced
    thinly with peel on
2 cups mushrooms, sliced thin
3 to 4 tablespoons liquid aminos
1 red pepper, sliced into 1-inch strips
2 medium carrots, shredded
1 recipe basic quinoa (page 100), already
    cooked

1. In a large skillet, sauté onion and celery until they begin to brown.

2. Add zucchini, squash, mushrooms and liquid aminos, and stir-fry until crisp tender, about 6 minutes. (Use liquid aminos to taste; they are salty.)

3. Just before serving, stir in red pepper, carrots and quinoa.

Makes 10 one-cup servings

Nutrients per serving: Calories 118, Protein 4g, Carbohydrate 22g, Fat 4g, Cholesterol 0mg, Saturated Fat trace, Sodium 388mg, Dietary Fiber 3g

Friends are angels who lift our feet when our own wings have trouble remembering how to fly.
—Unknown

Garden Harvest Menu

Stuffed Summer Squash

Curried Corn Bisque

Veggie Tuna
Recipe in Potpourri: Cooking with Carrots

Raspberry-Glazed Summer Fruit Tart

Watermelon-Ginger Marmalade

Peach Julep
Recipe in Healthy Drinks

Pictured, clockwise from top left: Peach Julep (page 83), Raspberry-Glazed Summer Fruit Tart, Stuffed Summer Squash, Veggie Tuna (page 90), Curried Corn Bisque

Stuffed SUMMER SQUASH

You can prepare this dish early in the day, cover, and chill. Pop it in the oven right before dinner.

4 to 5 medium yellow summer squash
½ teaspoon salt
2 tablespoons olive oil
1 small onion, chopped
2 carrots, shredded
⅔ cup broccoli, chopped fine
½ cup red bell pepper, chopped fine
Reserved squash pulp
¾ teaspoon garlic salt
Pinch of cayenne (optional)
1 tablespoon liquid aminos

1. Drop squash and salt into boiling water. Boil 10 minutes. Cool squash on paper towels.

2. Cut squash in half lengthwise; scoop out pulp, leaving ½-inch thick shells. Reserve pulp.

3. Heat oil and sauté onion until tender. Add other veggies and reserved pulp; sauté 2 minutes. Add garlic salt, cayenne and liquid aminos. Spoon into squash shells and place in a 9 x 13-inch pan. Bake at 325 degrees F for 20 to 25 minutes.

Serves 10

Nutrients per serving: Calories 62, Protein 2g, Carbohydrate 8g, Fat 3g, Cholesterol 0mg, Saturated Fat trace, Sodium 337mg, Dietary Fiber 2.5g

Curried CORN BISQUE

1 tablespoon olive oil
1 large onion, chopped coarse
3 cups fresh or frozen (thawed) corn
  kernels
1 teaspoon curry powder
½ teaspoon salt
⅛ teaspoon cayenne
1 box (12.3 ounces) extra-firm, silken tofu
2 cups water
2 teaspoons vegetable broth and soup
  mix
¼ cup green onion, top part, thinly sliced

1. Heat oil in a large pot over medium heat. Add onion, corn, curry powder, salt and cayenne. Cook and stir for 10 minutes until onions begin to brown. Remove from heat.

2. Drain tofu. Put into a blender or food processor and blend to smooth. Scrape down sides.

3. Add half of the cooked corn mixture and half of the water; blend with the tofu to smooth.

4. Add tofu mixture back to sautéed veggies, reserving ½ cup of the onion-corn mixture for garnish. Stir in remaining water and vegetable broth mix. Heat through.

5. Serve each bowl garnished with 1 tablespoon green onion and one spoonful of reserved onion-corn mixture.

Serves 4

Nutrients per serving: Calories 210, Protein 11g, Carbohydrate 31g, Fat 7g, Cholesterol 0mg, Saturated Fat trace, Sodium 817mg, Dietary Fiber 5g

Raspberry-Glazed
SUMMER FRUIT TART

This tart is easily changeable depending on seasonal fruit.

CRUST:
2 cups whole-wheat pastry flour
⅓ cup sucanat
1½ teaspoons Rumford's aluminum-free
   baking powder
⅓ cup canola oil
⅛ cup plus 1 teaspoon Hokan Lite
   coconut milk
2 teaspoons pure vanilla

FILLING:
1 cup seedless all-fruit raspberry or
   blackberry jam
1 large peach, blanched, peeled and
   seeded
1 large, tart apple, peeled, seeded and cut
   into ¼-inch slices
1 kiwi, peeled and thinly sliced
¼ cup fresh blueberries (optional)

1. Gently spoon the flour into the measuring cup and level off with a knife.

2. In a medium bowl combine flour, sucanat and baking powder.

3. Using a pastry blender, cut in oil until pea-sized pieces form. Add coconut milk and vanilla to flour mixture, stirring just until combined.

4. Gently knead 12 to 15 strokes until a ball forms. Cover with plastic wrap and chill for 1 hour.

5. Crumble chilled dough evenly over an 11-inch tart pan with removable bottom. Pat dough evenly on bottom and sides. Prick with a fork and bake at 375 degrees F for 25 minutes. Cool on wire rack.

6. Melt jam in a small saucepan. Using a pastry brush, brush some of the jam over the entire crust, coating it well.

7. Arrange peeled and thinly sliced fruit in a circular fashion on bottom of crust. Generously brush, then pour, the remaining jam over the fruit.

Serves 10

Nutrients per serving: Calories 280, Protein 4g, Carbohydrate 52g, Fat 8g, Cholesterol 0mg, Saturated Fat 1g, Sodium 55mg, Dietary Fiber 4g

Watermelon-Ginger
MARMALADE

1 lemon
1 tablespoon minced fresh ginger
8 cups watermelon, peeled, seeded and
   cut into ½-inch cubes
2½ cups Welch's 100 percent white grape
   juice concentrate
½ cup Minute tapioca

1. To prepare the spice bag: Zest the lemon. Cut the lemon in half and squeeze out the juice. Reserve the juice for later in the recipe.

2. Holding a squeezed lemon half in your hand, carefully cut away and discard the remaining white rind.

3. Cut the pulpy sections into 2 or 3 pieces. Repeat with remaining half. Put pulp and ginger into a cloth tea bag; tie with string.

4. In a large non-aluminum Dutch oven, cook watermelon, finely minced lemon zest and spice bag over medium heat for 30 minutes, stirring occasionally.

5. Add grape juice, lemon juice and tapioca. Bring to a low boil, stirring often until tapioca is no longer white in the middle, about 25 minutes.

6. Squeeze spice bag between two spoons to remove juices. Discard.

7. Pour marmalade into hot sterilized jam jars, filling to ½ inch to ¼ inch from the top; wipe jar rims. Cover at once with metal lids, screw on bands and process in a boiling water bath for 10 minutes. Make sure lids seal.

Makes 64 one-tablespoon servings (2 pints)

Nutrients per serving: Calories 27, Protein 0g, Carbohydrate 7g, Fat 0g, Cholesterol 0mg, Saturated Fat 0g, Sodium 3mg, Dietary Fiber trace

Why not go out on a limb? That's where the fruit is.
—Mark Twain

Thanksgiving Menu

Pumpkin Soup

Roasted Autumn Vegetables

Sweet Potato Bake

Red Onion-Cranberry Relish

Vegan Mashed Potatoes

Pan Gravy

Cornbread Stuffing

Cranberry Cobblestone Bread & Dinner Rolls

Pumpkin Foamy

The Best Pumpkin Pie

Apple Upside-Down Pie

Whole-Grain Pie Crust

Clockwise, from upper left: Pumpkin Soup, Cranberry Cobblestone Bread & Dinner Rolls, Apple Upside-Down Pie, Red Onion-Cranberry Relish, Cornbread Stuffing, Roasted Autumn Vegetables, Vegan Mashed Potatoes with Pan Gravy

Pumpkin Soup

Make a pumpkin serving bowl for a beautiful centerpiece on your holiday table to take the place of the turkey.

¼ cup canola oil
½ cup finely chopped green pepper
¼ cup chopped green onion, white part only
2 tablespoon chopped fresh parsley
¼ teaspoon thyme leaves
2 bay leaves
2 cups Hunt's Choice-Cut diced tomatoes
1 large can (30 ounces) solid pack pumpkin
4 teaspoons McKay's chicken-style seasoning
4 cups water
⅛ cup whole-wheat pastry flour
4 cups vanilla-flavored almond milk, divided
2 teaspoon salt
Pie pumpkins as serving bowls (optional)

1. Sauté in oil, but do not brown, the pepper, onion, parsley, thyme and bay leaves.

2. Add tomatoes, pumpkin, seasoning and water; bring to a boil. Reduce heat and simmer 30 minutes.

3. In a separate bowl, whisk together flour and 1 cup of the almond milk. Add to soup along with the remaining 3 cups of milk and salt. Stir over medium heat until mixture boils. Serve hot.

To make the serving bowl:

To use a pumpkin as a serving bowl, select an 8- to 10-pound pumpkin, rub with canola oil, and place on a baking sheet in the oven at 325 degrees F for 45 to 50 minutes. Small pie pumpkins can be used as individual bowls and should be baked for 25 minutes at the same temperature. The pumpkins will become just soft enough to cut the top off easily with a v-shaped cutter. Scoop out the insides and discard, or save seeds for later roasting. Fill pumpkin with hot soup just before serving. Decorate the bottom of your platter with some pressed colorful leaves.

Makes 15 one-cup servings

Nutrients per serving: Calories 86, Protein 2g, Carbohydrate 11g, Fat 4.5g, Cholesterol 0mg, Saturated Fat trace, Sodium 525mg, Dietary Fiber 2g

Roasted Autumn Vegetables

2 ears of sweet corn on the cob, shucked and washed
1 large or 2 medium zucchini, quartered lengthwise
2 medium yellow summer squash, quartered lengthwise
2 medium to small turnips, peeled and cut into 4 wedges
1 large red onion, cut into 4 wedges
6 to 8 tablespoons olive oil
Salt

1. Wash and cut vegetables according to directions. Place veggies into a 9 x 13-inch baker, drizzle with oil and salt to taste.

2. Broil on low for 35 to 40 minutes, turning vegetables every 5 or 6 minutes. Vegetables are done when they begin to brown and look roasted.

Serves 13

Nutrients per serving: Calories 92, Protein 2g, Carbohydrate 8g, Fat 7g, Cholesterol 0mg, Saturated Fat trace, Sodium 11mg, Dietary Fiber 2g

Sweet Potato
BAKE

2 cans (29 ounces each) cut yams in light
  syrup, drained
¾ cup pure maple syrup
1 teaspoon pure vanilla
⅛ cup canola oil
⅓ cup and ½ cup vanilla-flavored
  almond milk
2 tablespoons flax seeds

1. Place yams, maple syrup, vanilla, oil and
⅓ cup of the almond milk in mixer on a medium
speed, and mix well.

2. In blender on high speed, blend flax seeds
and remaining almond milk for 2 minutes.
Scrape down sides of your blender and blend
again until mixture becomes very thick, about
2 more minutes.

3. Place flax mixture in a large glass measuring
cup and cook in microwave on high for
1½ minutes (will bubble).

4. Pour flax mixture into the sweet potato mixture, and beat until light and fluffy-looking. Put
into a round 10- or 11-inch quiche pan. Cover
with topping (below) and bake at 350 degrees F
for 30 minutes.

TOPPING:
½ cup sucanat
½ cup whole-wheat pastry flour
1 cup coarsely chopped pecans
¼ cup canola oil

1. Mix sucanat, flour and pecans together well.
Coat with oil and mix to form crumb topping.

2. Sprinkle over sweet potato bake and bake as
above. Topping will brown in oven.

Serves 18

*Nutrients per serving: Calories 239, Protein 2g,
Carbohydrate 35g, Fat 9g, Cholesterol 0mg,
Saturated Fat 1g, Sodium 42mg, Dietary Fiber 3g*

Red Onion-
CRANBERRY RELISH

1 large red onion, thinly sliced into rings
1 tablespoon canola oil
¼ cup raisins
¼ cup any berry-flavor all-fruit fruit juice
  (I use Welch's white grape-raspberry)
Salt
¾ cup pure maple syrup
4 inches stick cinnamon
1 cup water
1 package (12 ounces) fresh or frozen
  cranberries, washed and sorted
2 tablespoons cornstarch
½ cup juice, reserved from the onion-
  cranberry mixture

1. Sauté onion in oil until tender and just beginning to brown, about 5 minutes.

2. Combine raisins, juice and a dash of salt in a
saucepan and simmer 10 minutes uncovered. Add
to above and cook 1 minute. Remove from heat
and set aside.

3. Combine maple syrup, cinnamon and water in
a saucepan.

4. Add the berries to the syrup-cinnamon-water
mixture and bring to a low boil. Cook just until
berries pop. (If you cook too long, the berries will
open up and all the seeds will come out.)

5. Pour the juice and berry mixture into the
frying pan with the onion mixture.

6. Remove approximately ½ cup of the juice from
the pan and stir in the cornstarch until well
blended. Add the cornstarch mixture back to the
onion and cranberries, and bring to a low boil
to thicken. Remove cinnamon stick and serve.
Absolutely delicious!

Makes 9 half-cup servings

*Nutrients per serving: Calories 131, Protein 1g,
Carbohydrate 30g, Fat 1.5g, Cholesterol 0mg,
Saturated Fat trace, Sodium 5mg, Dietary Fiber 1g*

*Come, ye thankful
people, come,
Raise the song of
Harvest-home;
All is safely
gathered in,
Ere the winter
storms begin.
—Henry Alford*

Vegan Mashed Potatoes

2½ to 3 pounds medium to small
red-skinned potatoes, with skins
Water
2 to 2½ teaspoons salt
1 cup original or vanilla-flavored
almond milk

1. Wash and scrub potatoes removing any bad spots. Cut into medium-sized pieces. Add enough water just to cover, and add salt. Boil on medium heat until soft when pierced with the tip of a knife. Discard water.

2. Put potatoes into a mixing bowl and add the almond milk. Blend until fairly smooth. The beaters will actually remove about half of the skins for you, but your mashed potatoes will still have a rustic look.

Serves 14

Nutrients per serving: Calories 89, Protein 2g, Carbohydrate 20g, Fat trace, Cholesterol 0mg, Saturated Fat trace, Sodium 163mg, Dietary Fiber 2g

Pan Gravy

1 large onion, diced fine
¼ cup canola oil
⅜ cup (¼ + ⅛) whole-wheat pastry flour
2 cups water
2 teaspoons McKay's chicken-style
seasoning
½ teaspoon salt

1. Sauté onion in oil until dark brown.

2. Add flour and allow to become very brown. Have the liquids ready to pour in at just the right moment.

3. Mix together water, seasoning and salt, and microwave for 3 minutes.

4. Stir quickly into browned mixture. (Will thicken as it boils.)

Makes about 3 cups.

Serves 14

Nutrients per serving: Calories 53, Protein 1g, Carbohydrate 4g, Fat 4g, Cholesterol 0mg, Saturated Fat trace, Sodium 144mg, Dietary Fiber 1g

Cornbread Stuffing

1 cup finely chopped red onion
1 cup finely chopped celery
1 cup finely chopped yellow summer
squash
⅛ cup canola oil
¾ teaspoon thyme leaves
¼ teaspoon nutmeg
1 teaspoon salt
4 cups dry cornbread stuffing, generic or
Pepperidge Farm
1¼ cup water
1¼ teaspoons McKay's chicken-style
seasoning

1. Sauté onion, celery and squash in oil till tender, then add thyme, nutmeg and salt.

2. When seasonings are mixed in, add the cornbread stuffing and toss to mix.

3. Mix and boil water and seasoning, pour over stuffing and mix with spoon. Cover and let stand for 5 minutes before serving. If you need to reheat this, you can sauté it in a frying pan or cover tightly and heat in your oven.

Makes 11 half-cup servings

Nutrients per serving: Calories 168, Protein 5g, Carbohydrate 33g, Fat 2g, Cholesterol 0mg, Saturated Fat 0g, Sodium 964mg, Dietary Fiber 1g

Cranberry Cobblestone
BREAD & DINNER ROLLS

This dough recipe is to be divided in half after you have mixed it up. Half will make 1 large loaf of cranberry cobblestone bread, and the other half will make 16 dinner rolls.

8 to 9 cups whole-wheat pastry flour, divided
4 teaspoons yeast
2½ cups warm water (120 to 130 degrees F)
2 tablespoons canola oil
2 teaspoons salt
½ cup honey
½ cup plus ⅛ cup fresh or frozen cranberries, chopped medium to fine in food processor (measure before chopping)
½ cup pure maple syrup
4 teaspoons ground cinnamon

1. Mix together 6 cups of the flour and yeast in a large bowl.

2. Whisk together the water, oil, salt and honey in a separate bowl. Add to the flour and yeast mixture.

3. Knead with dough hooks in your mixer (or by hand) for 7 to 10 minutes to form the gluten.

4. Add the last 2 to 3 cups of flour, just enough to take away stickiness. Cover dough and allow to rise once.

5. In a large bowl, combine cranberries, maple syrup and cinnamon.

6. Cut dough in half. Cover one half and set aside for rolls.

To make the loaf:

1. Punch down dough. Using kitchen cutters, cut dough into ¾-inch pieces and drop into cranberry mixture. Stir mixture after every 8 to 10 new pieces of dough so each piece gets coated.

2. When finished, put dough into a large oiled loaf pan and allow to rise almost to double. Bake at 375 degrees F for 40 to 45 minutes. Top will begin to brown.

To make the rolls:

Cut remaining dough into 16 two-inch pieces and form into balls. Bake in an 8 x 8-inch oiled baking pan at 375 degrees F for about 25 minutes.

Serves 50

Nutrients per serving: Calories 87, Protein 3g, Carbohydrate 17g, Fat 1g, Cholesterol 0mg, Saturated Fat 0g, Sodium 78mg, Dietary Fiber 3g

Because your love is better than life, my lips will glorify you.
—Psalm 63:3

Pumpkin FOAMY

The Best PUMPKIN PIE

O, it sets my heart
a-clickin' like the
tickin' of a clock,
When the frost is on
the punkin and the
fodder's in the shock.

—James
Whitcomb Riley

1 cup vanilla-flavored almond milk
1 medium banana, broken into pieces
¼ cup solid-pack pumpkin
Dash or two of cinnamon
2 tablespoons pure maple syrup
4 ice cubes

Place everything except ice cubes in blender; blend till smooth. Add ice cubes and blend again.

Makes two 10-ounce servings.

Nutrients per serving: Calories 150, Protein 2g, Carbohydrate 34g, Fat 1.5g, Cholesterol 0mg, Saturated Fat 0g, Sodium 55mg, Dietary Fiber 2g

THE BENEFITS OF CANNED PUMPKIN

According to Heinerman's Encyclopedia of Healing Juices, *one pound of canned pumpkin pulp contains the following nutrients: 113 mg calcium, 118 mg phosphorus, 1.8 mg iron, 9 mg sodium, 1,089 mg potassium, 29,030 IU vitamin A, 2.7 mg niacin, 23 mg vitamin C, and 66 mg magnesium.*

Dr. Heinerman has used raw pumpkin juice in the treatment of leukemia and AIDS. His book includes many interesting stories.

Heinerman's Encyclopedia of Healing Juices, Parker Publishing Company: West Nyack, N.Y.

My first Taste of Health recipe! This pie will fool the most finicky of eaters.

1¼ cup pure maple syrup
2 teaspoons pure vanilla
½ teaspoon salt
1 teaspoon cinnamon
2½ cups mashed silken, extra-firm Lite Mori-Nu tofu (drain off any water)
1 can (15 ounces) solid-pack pumpkin
1 whole-grain pie crust (recipe at right)

1. In a blender, combine maple syrup, vanilla, salt and cinnamon till smooth. Then blend in tofu, 1 cup at a time, until smooth.

2. Pour mixture into a mixing bowl and, using beaters, blend in pumpkin.

3. Pour pumpkin mixture into one unbaked 9-inch crust.

4. Lightly sprinkle top of pie with cinnamon and bake at 350 degrees F for 1 hour and 10 minutes. Refrigerate before serving. Allow flavors to blend and pie tastes much richer. Top with a dollop of tofu whipped cream (page 82).

Serves 8

Nutrients per serving: Calories 383, Protein 10g, Carbohydrate 66g, Fat 8g, Cholesterol 0mg, Saturated Fat 1g, Sodium 377mg, Dietary Fiber 6g

Apple UPSIDE-DOWN PIE

Looks beautiful and tastes even better!

GLAZE & PASTRY:
¼ **cup pure maple syrup**
⅓ **cup pecan halves, coarsely chopped**
1 **whole-grain pie crust (recipe at right)**

1. Pour syrup onto the bottom of a 9-inch pie plate. Sprinkle pecans over bottom.

2. Place one rolled-out pie shell over the nut mixture. Gently press dough down sides of pie plate making sure there are no air bubbles trapped under dough. Don't cut off overhanging dough. Prepare filling.

FILLING:
3 **tablespoons whole-wheat pastry flour**
1 **teaspoon ground cinnamon**
4 **large, fresh Granny Smith or tart pie apples, peeled and sliced ¼-inch thick**
½ **cup pure maple syrup**

1. Sprinkle flour and cinnamon over apples, and toss well to coat.

2. Pour maple syrup over apples and mix well again. Put apples into pie shell, and cover with top pastry.

3. Fold top crust under edge of bottom crust and pinch well to seal. Cut two slits in top of pie to let steam escape. Bake at 400 degrees F for 50 to 60 minutes. (Place a cookie sheet on rack below pie to catch any drips. Don't place pie plate directly on cookie sheet.) When pie is done, allow it to sit for 5 minutes.

4. Put a glass platter on top of the pie and flip the two dishes over. Gently lift the pie plate up until the pie releases. Scrape any stuck-on pecans off the bottom of the pie plate and put them back on the pie. Serve warm.

Serves 8

Nutrients per serving: Calories 379, Protein 7g, Carbohydrate 64g, Fat 12g, Cholesterol 0mg, Saturated Fat 2g, Sodium 204mg, Dietary Fiber 8g

Whole Grain PIE CRUST

Recipe makes two 9-inch pie crusts. Make half this recipe for a single-crust pie.

1¼ **cup quick oats (blended into flour in your blender)**
1 **cup whole-wheat pastry flour**
¾ **teaspoon salt**
¼ **cup canola oil**
½ **cup water**

1. In a medium bowl place oats, flour and salt.

2. With your hands, rub in canola oil.

3. Pour water into bowl. Mix well. Will look too wet at first, but this is the perfect amount of water.

4. Knead lightly on counter with hands, not adding any flour.

5. Wipe counter with a damp cloth, and stick a piece of plastic wrap about 15 inches long to your countertop.

6. Sprinkle about 1 teaspoon of whole-wheat pastry flour on plastic wrap. Divide dough in half (recipe makes two crusts).

7. Flatten into circle, cover with another piece of plastic wrap and roll out with your rolling pin until about ¾ inch bigger in diameter than your pie plate. Remove top piece of plastic wrap and center the crust on the pie plate. Remove remaining piece of plastic.

8. Prick crust with fork on bottom and edges. Trim off any excess dough and fill crust with your favorite filling, or bake at 350 degrees F for 12 to 15 minutes.

Serves 8

Nutrients per serving: Calories 206, Protein 2g, Carbohydrate 27g, Fat 9g, Cholesterol 0mg, Saturated Fat 1g, Sodium 201mg, Dietary Fiber 5g

Laughter is the language of the young at heart. And you know what? You don't have to be happy to laugh. You become happy because you laugh.
—Barbara Johnson

HOME FOR THE HOLIDAYS
A CHRISTMAS MENU

CHRISTMAS CRUNCH SALAD

EASY BERRY RELISH

MEATLESS "JINGLE" BALLS

PORTOBELLO MUSHROOMS WITH CARAMELIZED ONIONS

ROMANIAN EGGPLANT SPREAD

VEGAN MASHED POTATOES WITH PAN GRAVY
RECIPE IN THANKSGIVING SECTION

CRANBERRY COBBLESTONE BREAD & DINNER ROLLS

CRANBERRY FRUIT SQUARES

HOT STRAWBERRY CIDER

THE BEST CAROB FUDGE PIE
RECIPE IN POTPOURRI: COOKING WITH CAROB

CAROB FUDGE
RECIPE IN POTPOURRI: COOKING WITH CAROB

*Pictured, clockwise from bottom left: Easy Berry Relish,
Hot Strawberry Cider, The Best Carob Fudge (page 97),
Orange-Sugared Pecans, Portobello Mushrooms with
Caramelized Onions, Christmas Crunch Salad, Meatless
"Jingle" Balls*

Christmas
CRUNCH SALAD

As we each celebrate the holidays this year, it is my prayer that we will be able to fill our bodies with healthful, yet absolutely wonderful food that the Lord has provided. It is my sincere desire to keep health "reform" from becoming health "deform." Please keep my Taste of Health ministry in your prayers.

4 cups broccoli, 1-inch pieces
4 cups cauliflower, 1-inch pieces
2 cups cherry tomatoes, cut in half
    (or cubed plum tomatoes)
1½ cups Vegenaise
2 tablespoons honey
2 tablespoons lemon juice
Paprika

1. Put veggies into a large bowl.

2. Mix up Vegenaise, honey and lemon juice, and pour over the vegetables. Toss well to coat. Sprinkle with paprika and serve cold.

Serves 20

Nutrients per serving: Calories 130, Protein 1g, Carbohydrate 6g, Fat 11g, Cholesterol 0mg, Saturated Fat 1g, Sodium 106mg, Dietary Fiber 1g

Easy
BERRY RELISH

This dish is very pretty displayed on your holiday table.

1 package (12 ounces) fresh or frozen cranberries
1 can (12 ounces) Welch's white grape-raspberry 100 percent juice concentrate
1⅔ cups sparkling grape juice (look for a brand that uses fruit juice to sweeten)
⅓ cup lemon juice
1 package (3.39 ounces) Hain Super Fruits strawberry dessert mix

1. In a saucepan, combine cranberries, juice concentrate, grape juice and lemon juice. Cook over medium heat just until berries pop, about 10 minutes. Do *not* cook too long as berries will open up and the seeds spill out, and your dish will not be as pretty.

2. Remove from heat and stir in dessert mix until dissolved.

3. Pour into glass serving bowl and chill overnight. It will have the consistency of soft jam. Makes about 5 cups.

Serves 23

Nutrients per serving: Calories 73, Protein trace, Carbohydrate 19g, Fat trace, Cholesterol 0mg, Saturated Fat trace, Sodium 2mg, Dietary Fiber 0g

Meatless
"JINGLE" BALLS

These make great hors d'oeuvres. Stick a frilled toothpick into each meatball and arrange on a platter with a small dish of sauce in the middle for dipping.

1¼ cups cornbread stuffing, generic or Pepperidge Farm
¾ cup pecan meal
⅓ cup minced fresh parsley (do not use dried)
1 large sweet onion, finely chopped and browned in skillet in 1 tablespoon oil
½ teaspoon ground cumin
1 teaspoon sweet basil
½ teaspoon oregano
2 tablespoons liquid aminos
½ cup water
1 teaspoon McKay's chicken-style seasoning
2 tablespoons flax seeds

1. Combine cornbread stuffing, pecan meal and parsley in a bowl.

2. Brown the onion very brown, then add cumin, basil, oregano and liquid aminos. When onions are well-coated, add onion mixture to the cornbread mixture.

3. In a blender, blend water, seasoning and flax seeds for 2 minutes. Scrape down sides of blender and blend until mixture gets very thick, about 2 more minutes.

4. Put flax mixture into a glass measuring cup, being careful to get most of it out of the blender, and cook in your microwave for 1½ minutes. When mixture is cooked, add it to the above cornbread mixture and mix well.

5. Using a 1-tablespoon scoop, form balls on a 12 x 15-inch rectangle baking stone or cookie sheet, and bake at 350 degrees F for 25 minutes.

SAUCE:
1 jar (10 ounces) Smuckers all-fruit seedless blackberry or black-raspberry jam
1 jar (28 ounces) Classico sun-dried tomato sauce, or favorite

1. Melt jam in a medium saucepan. Add tomato sauce and mix well.

2. Spoon over meatballs when you serve.

Serving note: If you are going to eat all the meatballs, you can add them to the sauce right before serving. If you think you will have leftovers, have your guests ladle the sauce over their meatballs individually.

Makes 60 single-meatball servings

Nutrients per serving: Calories 51, Protein 1g, Carbohydrate 6g, Fat 4g, Cholesterol 0mg, Saturated Fat trace, Sodium 104mg, Dietary Fiber 0g

*Blessed is the season which engages the whole world in a conspiracy of love.
—Hamilton Wright Mabie*

Portobello
MUSHROOMS WITH
CARAMELIZED ONIONS

*Home is where
one starts from.*
—T. S. Eliot

1 large onion, sliced into thin rings and
  separated
2 tablespoons canola oil
2 tablespoons liquid aminos
3 portobello mushrooms, sliced ½-inch
  thick
¼ cup water mixed with ½ teaspoon
  McKay's chicken-style seasoning

1. Brown onion in oil in skillet.

2. Add liquid aminos and mushrooms.

3. Pour the water mixture over the mushrooms
and cover skillet. Simmer on low 5 minutes, until
mushrooms are tender.

To serve, place onions on the bottom of your
bowl and arrange the mushrooms neatly lined up
over the top.

Serves 5

*Nutrients per serving: Calories 83, Protein 2g,
Carbohydrate 11g, Fat 6g, Cholesterol 0mg,
Saturated Fat trace, Sodium 313mg, Dietary Fiber 1g*

Romanian
EGGPLANT SPREAD

*This spread has a delicate smoked flavor, and is
great on toast or light bread, or as a vegetable dip.
Me? I eat it with a spoon!*

2 medium to large soft eggplants, makes
  3 to 4 cups cooked
⅓ cup very finely chopped white onion
⅓ to ½ cup canola oil
Salt, about 1 teaspoon
1 to 2 tablespoons lemon juice (optional)
  can replace some of the fat

1. Roast eggplants over an open flame. I put
foil under the burners on my gas stove to catch
the drips. You can roast these on an open fire
outside, using a rack to hold them up off of the
flame a little bit, or you can use your grill. Turn
the eggplants about every 5 minutes until the
outside skin is well charred and all sides have
been pretty evenly cooked.

2. Allow to cool slightly (not several hours), and
holding the eggplant by the top, begin carefully
pulling the outer skin off. Do not rinse your
eggplant under water.

3. When the skin is removed, lay the eggplant
on a clean plate and press lightly to remove
excess juice. Discard juice. If you cooked your
eggplant too long there will be very little "meat"
inside. You want to cook it, but not overcook it.
It has a way of evaporating!

4. Put eggplant, oil and salt into a food processor
to blend into a fine and delicate paste.

5. Add the onion after blending, stir and serve in
a bowl with sliced tomatoes around the edge for
garnish.

Serves 8

*Nutrients per serving: Calories 94, Protein trace,
Carbohydrate 3g, Fat 9g, Cholesterol 0mg,
Saturated Fat <1g, Sodium 268mg, Dietary Fiber 1g*

Cranberry
FRUIT SQUARES

This dense, moist recipe takes the place of fruit bread.

2 cups whole-wheat pastry flour
½ cup oat bran
½ cup cornmeal
1 teaspoon ground coriander
¾ teaspoon salt
¼ cup canola oil
2¼ cup fresh or frozen cranberries
    coarsely chopped in food processor
1 cup sliced almonds
1 cup rinsed raisins (I always rinse my
    raisins in hot tap water)
1¼ cup water
¾ cup pure maple syrup
2 tablespoon molasses
2 teaspoon vanilla

1. Combine flour, oat bran, cornmeal, coriander and salt in a bowl. Rub in canola oil with your hands until lumps are removed.

2. Add cranberries, almonds and raisins, and toss well to coat.

3. In a separate bowl whisk together water, maple syrup, molasses and vanilla until all are dissolved. Mix everything together and put into a deep-dish stoneware baker or a 10-inch quiche pan. Bake at 300 degrees F for 50 to 60 minutes, just until set and not wet on top. Cut into 1-inch squares to serve.

Makes 50 one-ounce servings

Nutrients per serving: Calories 71, Protein 1.5g, Carbohydrate 12g, Fat 2g, Cholesterol 0mg, Saturated Fat trace, Sodium 34mg, Dietary Fiber 1g

Hot
STRAWBERRY CIDER

This drink is a beautiful red color.

8 cups cider
1 teaspoon whole cloves
4 inches stick cinnamon
1 bag (1 pound) frozen strawberries

1. Bring all ingredients to a boil. Reduce to low heat and simmer uncovered for 10 minutes.

2. Pour cider through a fine strainer to remove berry pulp. Serve hot.

Serves 9

Nutrients per serving: Calories 102, Protein 0g, Carbohydrate 7g, Fat trace, Cholesterol 0mg, Saturated Fat trace, Sodium 1mg, Dietary Fiber 1g

What is more agreeable than one's home?
—Marcus Tullius Cicero

BARB'S DRUG-FREE CROHN'S CONTROL

Discuss with your doctor any changes you may want to make in your diet or exercise program.

Dear Friends,

I just want to take a minute to thank all of you from the bottom of my heart for the wonderful letters of encouragement you have written to me! Many of you have asked for my "Crohn's recipes," or information on what I have done for Crohn's myself. That is one of the biggest reasons for this letter—and this cookbook.

When I was asked to give my Crohn's and colitis testimony on a Three Angels Broadcasting Network "3ABN Presents" special in May 1997, I explained to the staff that I thought my story was needed, but that it would be somewhat graphic. I was afraid of possibly offending someone by talking so frankly. But I feel that there are many people in this world who are suffering and don't know where to turn or what to do, and they are too embarrassed to ask for help. I know I was at one time. I am currently working on putting my testimony in print. Hopefully that project will be completed sometime during the year 2001.

I have had Crohn's disease for 19 years. Crohn's is an inflammatory bowel disease that causes inflammation and ulceration of your small or large intestine. It may cause chronic diarrhea, abdominal pain, urgency (when you feel there isn't enough time to make it to the bathroom), rectal bleeding, bloodloss anemia, incontinence of stool and fistula disease. Those who suffer usually suffer silently. It's an embarrassing disease that is not talked about. My goal is to change all that and to let the world know there is hope!

In October 1994, doctors removed my extremely scarred large intestine and rectum. I felt as though I had been defeated and that I would never be able to help anyone else. At that point I had been medication-free for one year and three months. However, the day before my surgery I had my last colonoscopy, a test in which a tube with a small camera is inserted into the rectum to view you from the inside out. The test showed that approximately two-thirds of my large intestine, which had previously been 100 percent ulcerated, had totally healed. Unfortunately, years of scar tissue had developed in my descending colon and rectum, making them impossible to save. I gratefully live with an ileostomy now, thankful to be alive and able to help others. I have occasionally had flare-ups but can bring them under control in 24 hours or less. The following pages explain in detail how I have for six years now controlled Crohn's disease drug-free.

Please understand that I am *not* a doctor, nor can I prescribe anything for you or take you off any medication. I *can* share with you a little of what I have personally gone through and what I have found works for me. Most of what I use or do I learned by reading and by personal trial and error. You should discuss with your doctor any changes you may want to make.

ALOE VERA TO CONTROL INFLAMMATION

Daily. I drink 12 ounces of aloe vera juice every morning upon rising. I pour it and let it start to warm while I take my shower. Then it's not too hot, not too cold. I personally have found an inexpensive brand of aloe that tastes great, is cold-processed and field-grown and works for me. I buy Fruit of the Earth brand— usually priced at $7.97 per gallon—at Wal-Mart in the pharmacy section on the shelf. (I'm telling you this because health food stores charge upwards of $25 per gallon of aloe.) For best results, don't mix it with any juice. Sip it on an empty stomach. No, it doesn't taste like Kool-Aid, but it's not horrible either. Aloe works for me like an internal Band-Aid, soothing inflammation and hopefully helping some of you get off that last 10 milligrams of prednisone. Check out some reading material on aloe from your library, or you can purchase a book at your local health food or book store.

Acute flare-up. I drink 10 to 12 ounces of aloe vera juice four to five times per day and skip eating, usually for about 24 hours. If I do eat food, it's a piece of soft fruit like banana or grapes. This would also be an ideal time to drink a glass of vegetable juice that you made fresh in your juicer. A mixture of carrot, kale, parsley and celery is a great juice to drink (16 to 20 ounces), but any vegetables in your crisper will do. Just don't mix fruits and vegetables together in your juices or your meals. (That alone will give you bad gas pains.) Also, always use a superfine strainer to remove any pulp from your juice. According to Dr. Sung Min Im (the director of a juicing program I attended), if you remove the pulp, your body doesn't need to go through digestion to break it down, and more of the nutrition will reach your cellular level and feed your starving cells.

I still have flare-ups with my Crohn's; I had one at camp meeting in May 1997. I simply bought some aloe vera juice, started drinking and stopped eating. (I had been eating some wheat gluten meat-replacement products that week, which I really *do not* recommend when you have any colon trouble.) For the next couple of days I ate moderately soft raw food and got over my flare-up quickly. Within three to four days, I was fine. One great thing about aloe is that if you are constipated, it tends to make you regular and "clean house," and if you have "the runs" it may stop that and help you to bulk up. I truly love it and couldn't survive drug-free without it!

EXERCISING FOR HEALTH

Exercise is important for a healthy circulatory system and a healthy immune system. Any mild exercise will stimulate improved blood circulation, which moves nutrients and disease-fighting white blood cells through your body. I use the mini trampoline as a convenient, indoor way to achieve my exercise goals. You may enjoy walking or swimming more. Find a good low-impact form of exercise that you enjoy. Begin with just 2 to 3 minutes of exercise, if that is all you can manage. Allow yourself plenty of time to work up to increased levels of activity. If you can only walk around your house one time—start with that. Many forms of exercise are inexpensive—you don't have to purchase expensive equipment to meet your exercise needs. To begin my exercise program, I purchased a mini trampoline at a discount store.

When I get out of bed in the morning, before my shower and pouring a glass of aloe, I go into my rec room and bounce for 10 minutes on my mini trampoline. Now, before you say to yourself, "I could *never* do that," I want you to understand why physical exercise can assist your recovery from inflammatory bowel disease (IBD).

It doesn't matter what time of the day you exercise. I use my trampoline in the morning because that is when I can best fit it into my schedule, and because no matter how bad I might be feeling before I bounce, I *always* feel better by the time I'm done, and for the rest of the day!

When I first started on a mini trampoline, I could barely bounce for 30 seconds. During those first several months, I had to stop many times to run to my bathroom. But I would return 10 to 15 times each day and bounce for another 30 to 45 seconds at a time. Sometimes my stomach would be hurting terribly, so I would hold my stomach as tightly as I could to support it while I bounced. Now, I'm not talking about jumping up and down on the trampoline. I'm talking about a healthful bounce where you lift your heels up and down about an inch and bounce gently. Or a bounce where you bounce from one leg to the other, kind of like you're walking in place. Both types of bouncing are very low impact and accomplish the same thing. Bouncing to music makes the time go faster.

I can't stress enough how important regular exercise is to my success in being healthy. When I started bouncing, I had two recto-vaginal fistulas, no control over my rectal sphincter, and incontinence every time I changed positions. I had to stuff toilet paper you-know-where just to be able to bounce. Please know that I

From a letter:
I wanted to say thanks for sharing your health message with us. You're an answered prayer that saved my stepmother's bowels. What a thing to be known for, but so essential for life! [My stepmother] went years of only having BMs once every two to three weeks to every day after your suggested aloe juice usage. You are a Godsend.

understand from the bottom of my heart some of your concerns and will be praying for your success!

BARLEY GREEN

I usually pour my aloe right after I have bounced and am ready for my shower. I sip it while I finish getting ready in the morning. Then I go downstairs and make a glass of barley green. Now before you say, "This woman drinks too many things that are gross," please understand there's a reason behind everything I do.

I believe that juicing your fruits and vegetables, straining them, then drinking them immediately is one of the fastest ways to speed healing and recovery from any illness or disease. My favorite juice combination is a 16 to 20-ounce glass of carrot, kale and parsley juice. It takes approximately two pounds of carrots, two kale leaves and a small bunch of parsley the size of a fifty-cent piece. I peel my carrots to remove dirt and chemicals and rinse the other vegetables well. (At the close of this letter I will list some books I have found wonderfully helpful in my search for answers about health. But no matter what I've read, I have experimented on myself to see how it affects me.) Juicing takes about 20 to 30 minutes, depending on how much cleaning you have to do to your vegetables and juicer, and I don't always have that time, or I may need to go to the store for veggies. That's one reason I love barley green.

Yoshihide Hagiwara, M.D., a pharmacologist who invented barley green and wrote *Green Barley Essence*, has done ground-breaking research in this area. Once the head of Japan's largest drug manufacturing company, Dr. Hagiwara worked with mercury, which caused him to fall ill of mercury poisoning in 1963.

Dr. Hagiwara found through exhaustive research that the key to health is nutrition—not drugs—and that the nutrients essential to good health are most abundant in the green juices of vegetables. Young barley plants, he found, hold the greatest and most balanced nutrients of all. The juice is extracted from organically grown barley leaves harvested at their most beneficial stage and spray-dried at room temperature to retain all of the nutrients, including enzymes. This juice, which Dr. Hagiwara named barley green, contains at least 16 vitamins, 23 minerals and 20 enzymes, providing the cells with nutrition needed for optimal growth and functioning. He believes barley green goes directly to the bloodstream, where it feeds the cells and builds the immune system. Barley green is a vital part of my daily nutritional program, and I recommend it highly.

Dr. George Malkmus of Hallelujah Acres in Shelby, N.C., recommends that it be taken in a small amount of distilled water or dissolved dry in the mouth—not in juice or tablet form. I personally put two heaping teaspoons into 10 to 12 ounces of distilled water. I have never tried taking it dry.

Because barley green is in a powdered form, there are no juicers or vegetables to clean. Just mix in water and go. For those of you who have a busy morning, it could be the perfect answer for your schedule. Take it to work, and at 10:30 when everyone else is drinking diet colas and eating doughnuts, have a glass of barley green.

When I first started drinking it, I only took one heaping teaspoon in water; now I take two. Start with a little, and work your way up to more. It's a lot easier to be successful that way. Don't try to do too much at first and set yourself up for failure. Begin by adding two or three new simple things to your daily routine. Don't beat yourself up if you skip a day. I think you'll find, as I did, that I felt so much improvement in a fairly short amount of time that I had incentive to keep going.

I personally recommend two different brands: Dr. Hagiwara's Green Magma and a brand sold through Dr. George Malkmus made by AIM. For more information on how to order barley green, write Hallelujah Acres, P.O. Box 2388, Shelby, N.C. 28151. Or call (704) 481-1700; fax (704) 481-0345. Also ask for their free copy of *Back to the Garden* newsletter. It's great!

Please know that I understand from the bottom of my heart some of your concerns and will be praying for your success!

GARLIC

Because of raw garlic, I haven't needed a prescription for an antibiotic in five years! Whenever I run a fever or start to feel a bladder infection coming on, garlic helps get rid of it immediately. (Four capsules of cranberry fruit can also help with a urinary infection, not as an antibiotic, but to make your urine acidic so the bacteria find it difficult to survive in that environment.) Pick up a book on garlic at your health food store. You will simply be amazed at all its healing benefits. And it's priced right! You can find garlic at every grocery store.

Also, be sure to include lots of garlic in the foods you cook. Garlic is nutritionally dense and could benefit you if you include it in your diet.

ACTIVATED CHARCOAL AND BAD GAS

Some of you have written and said "Help! What do I do about bad gas problems?" It is a problem that can be very embarrassing! I'm sure you all have at least a couple of stories you wish you could forget. I do, too. Understanding why you have gas is half the problem. Inside your colon you have good bacteria and bad bacteria. Any yeast, parasite or bacteria (good or bad) will create gas from feeding off the nutrients in your colon. Yeast, for example, feeds on simple sugars. All carbohydrates are broken down into simple sugars. And of course, any time you consume just plain sugar in the form of cookies or whatever, you are also feeding them.

So what can you do? For a short-term treatment of intestinal gas, I use activated charcoal capsules. I buy them at a health food store (usually more expensive), a local co-op, or sometimes I can find them really cheap at flea markets. Get the capsules or powder, not the tablets; the tablets contain small amounts of sugar. When I have bad gas, I'll take four capsules once a twice a day, or whenever I am suffering from gas pains.

I also gave it to my son, Nathan, in the middle of a store after he consumed an unknown amount of liquid soap. Charcoal is often given in the emergency room when doctors have to pump someone's stomach. In cases of overdose, it helps remove harmful medications from the body. Pretty amazing stuff! We always carry a bottle in our glove box and in my purse for emergencies. For children who can't swallow pills, the capsules can be opened into a small amount of water, stirred and sipped with a straw. It doesn't have any taste. Don't try to put the powder on your tongue and swallow with water. It is so light that when you take a breath, you'll breathe it in.

Charcoal is an adsorptive, meaning as it travels through your body, it attaches to itself poisons, bacteria, debris, and even medication, carrying them out of your body on its way through. My dictionary defines *adsorb* as "to gather a gas, liquid, or dissolved substance on a surface in a condensed layer, as when charcoal adsorbs gases." So, if you take it for gas, remember it will remove and adsorb even the medication in your system. (Please consult your doctor before adding charcoal to your diet.) Activated charcoal should not be used as a long-term solution to your problem.

A PARASITE CLEANSE

A more helpful solution to the gas problem may be returning the good bacteria levels to normal in the colon. It's not impossible to do, and without this occurring, bowel problems may persist. As long as you continue to consume sugar, even simple sugars (you can't completely quit eating carbohydrates), you feed the yeast, or candida. I've gone on a powerful parasite cleanse several times. I have found a simple and most effective parasite-killing program that works for me. I use an herbal parasite killer called "Clear." You can find information in my resources section, page 128, under the Awareness Corporation listing.

A little friendly warning here might be helpful to you. Many parasites are microscopic; they cannot be seen by the naked eye as they leave your body. But many parasites are large. If you find large worms in the toilet, they will be dead! "Better out than in," I always say. One of my very healthy close family members passed a four-inch, fat, white worm within 24 hours

Garlic is nutritionally dense and could benefit you if you include it in your diet.

of taking the first Clear capsule. When that happens, you can't help but ask yourself, "How long was that in there?"

Children take a lesser dose of everything, so consider weight and age before determining how much Clear to give. When our 8-year-old son took the cleanse, the fourth day he passed a bunch of pin worms. I had no idea they were in there. You can't always tell!

The idea of having parasites is not a pleasant one. But you may not want to ignore the possibility. The above examples show how a few days of treatment may point out the existence of a problem. These two apparently healthy people were infested, yet symptom-free. If you have any questions about parasites, please discuss this with your doctor. There are stool tests and regular medications that are also available for treating parasitic infections.

While I'm attempting to kill my parasites, I also add nondairy acidophilus to my diet to make sure I'm replacing the good bacteria. Most health food stores, in the refrigerator section, carry a brand of powdered multi-acidophilus. Another excellent brand of powdered acidophilus is Ultra Dophilus DF. It has to be purchased through a doctor's office—a chiropractor may carry it—and it must be kept cold. To contact the distributor, Metagenics, see my resources section, page 128.

DISTILLED WATER

Just a note about what you are drinking. You wouldn't wash your dishes every night in a sink full of Coke, Pepsi or Mountain Dew, so don't wash your blood and body organs in it, either. You need pure water to make healthy blood. Water is in every cell in your body and is required for its proper performance.

How much are you drinking a day? F. Batmanghelidj, M.D., recommends an easy-to-remember formula: Drink half your body weight in ounces every day. If you weigh 140 pounds, you should be drinking 70 ounces of water daily. In his book, *Your Body's Many Cries for Water*, Dr. Batmanghelidj explains that we are not sick; we are thirsty. He also explains how our bodies

have many "thirst signals." Pain unrelated to trauma is one of them. So the next time you have a localized pain in your body, consider reaching for a glass of water instead of Tylenol. When I was on Azulfidine (sulfasalazine) four times per day, even though the bottle said to drink plenty of water, I never felt thirsty. I was drinking only about 4 ounces—½ cup—of water per day! It's a wonder I didn't die from dehydration.

Every time you consume a soft drink, the high acidity levels are neutralized by your body. They have to be! And, according to Dr. Sung Min Im, the sad way this happens is that when all of the readily available dietary calcium is used up, your bones will then give up calcium in order to neutralize the acid. You can actually contribute to osteoporosis at an early age by altering your bone density with soda pop. I want to cry when I see unknowing parents put pop into their baby's bottle to drink or watch a father give his 2-year-old son coffee at the breakfast table and laugh that he's a "real man."

Distilled water is my choice because, unlike tap water, which may be filled with all kinds of detergents and chemicals and pollutants, distilled water is just water, nothing else. Think of water as a big sponge going through your body sopping up the toxic spills. If the water you drink out of your tap has its sponge saturated by the pollutants already in it, that only leaves some of the water able to do its important job. When you drink distilled water, you have almost complete soaking action in your water. For more detailed information about the properties of water and its possible contaminants, read *Fit for Life* by Harvey and Marilyn Diamond.

SEARCHING FOR ANSWERS

I had been on Prednisone, Azulfidine (sulfasalazine), Flagyl (metronidazole) and Imuran (azathioprine) for several years when I felt my body just slipping away from me. I was a young woman with a husband and small child, and had a poor quality of life. At that time I was suffering with extreme lethargy, frequent diarrhea, rectal bleeding, incontinence of stool and urgency. I also had vaginal discharge of stool contents due to a recto-vaginal fistula, which affected my sexual self-esteem and my sexual relationship with my husband. Emotionally, I was apathetic, extremely irritable and somewhat depressed. The disease significantly affected my social life. I was afraid to socialize because of fear of diarrhea at unpredictable times. Even little things like going grocery shopping would elicit fear of diarrhea and incontinence. I never knew when I would have a good day. Living with Crohn's is similar to having the stomach flu all of the time.

Then one day my aunt gave me a little booklet called "Two Months To Live" by Jan Marcussen. The booklet was written mostly for cancer patients, but it explained how God has His own natural laws of health and healing. It told of the healing benefits of a raw juice fasting program (one supervised by a medical professional) and how people were finding relief from seemingly incurable diseases. No medical claims were being made; this was simply a natural alternative healthy life-style program that anyone could go through. According to the booklet, natural juices (carrot, spinach, apple, grape, etc.) cause your body to go through a cleansing effect where you detox and get rid of built-up poisons.

I flew to Florida where the clinic was and began the cleanse under medical supervision. I was suffering with a second recto-vaginal fistula that was trying to form. A fistula is formed when the inflammation in the bowel creates a tunnel from the bowel to whatever organ or structure is adjacent to it. In my case, it tunneled from the bowel to the vagina. As the fistula formed, I was plagued by a continuous boil-like sore in a very tender area. I couldn't sit down, it was painful to walk and after a month of misery (the gynecologist would not lance it), I was desperate for help.

My first day on juices was difficult! I wasn't used to drinking carrot and green juice and I especially wasn't used to drinking something every 30 minutes from 9 a.m. to 6 p.m. On a

juice fast, your body goes into an automatic cleanse and you find yourself running to the bathroom about every 15 minutes all day long. Don't despair though; that only happens for one to two days. Then, beginning on or around the second day, it is common to get a detox headache. This headache is dull and is also part of the detoxification. It also subsides, lasting anywhere from two to four days. After I got through the first week I felt more energy, had more color in my skin and just generally felt better.

The most amazing and convincing part for me was that by the end of the second day on juices, my boil was completely gone. No lump, no pain, no signs of an active fistula! I juiced for one month, eating salads and vegetable sandwiches only on the weekends. I returned home for two months and then went back to juice for an additional three weeks.

THE ESSENTIALS OF GOOD HEALTH

It was during my weeks at the clinic in Florida that I learned about proper nutrition and how important it is to consume *fresh* food at every meal. I also learned:

• Exercise is essential to survival; just do it. Start with small goals and work your way up.

• Drink half your body's weight in ounces of distilled water every day (that is, a 120-pound person should drink 60 ounces of water daily, assuming you don't have congestive heart failure or renal failure). Use common sense and consult your doctor.

• Get 10 to 15 minutes of sunshine every day. It only needs to be a 6-inch area to reap the benefits, so the tops of your hands and your face are all you need to expose.

• Be temperate in your lifestyle. Eat in moderation, attend a stop-smoking clinic, replace alcohol with nonalcoholic beverages.

• Get plenty of fresh air. Most of us are shallow breathers. Make a habit of taking ten or more deep breaths while you are on your walk each day, while sitting at your desk working and just before bed. Spend time in nature.

• Get adequate rest. A good bedtime is not

Exercise is essential to survival; just do it. Start with small goals and work your way up.

optional if you want good health! Considerable amounts of body repairs are taking place from 9 p.m. to midnight. I've found that an hour of sleep before midnight is equivalent to two hours after.

• Trust in God to supply the answers for whatever problems you are going through. If you ask Him, He will help you.

A good bedtime is not optional if you want good health!

MY JUICE FAST SCHEDULE

Following is the generic juice fast program that I followed at the health clinic. I include this to give you an idea of the commitment required to undertake such a program. Please do not attempt a total juice fast without medical supervision.

9 a.m.	Lemon Water (6-8 ounces)
9:30 a.m.	Distilled Water (8 ounces)
10 a.m.	Lemon Water (6-8 ounces)
10:30 a.m.	Distilled Water (8 ounces)
11 a.m.	Carrot (6 ounces) + Spinach or Kale or Celery (2 ounces)
11:30 a.m.	Distilled Water (8 ounces)
Noon	Apple (4 ounces) + Grape (4 ounces)
1 p.m.	Carrot (6 ounces) + Spinach or Kale or Celery (2 ounces)
1:30 p.m.	Distilled Water (8 ounces)
2 p.m.	Carrot (6 ounces) + Spinach or Kale or Celery (2 ounces)
2:30 p.m.	Distilled Water (8 ounces)
3 p.m.	Carrot (6 ounces) + Spinach or Kale or Celery (2 ounces)
3:30 p.m.	Distilled Water (8 ounces)
4 p.m.	Carrot (6 ounces) + Spinach or Kale or Celery (2 ounces)
4:30 p.m.	Distilled Water (8 ounces)
5 p.m.	Lemon Water (6 to 8 ounces)
5:30 p.m.	Distilled Water (8 ounces)
6 p.m.	Lemon Water (6 to 8 ounces)

TIPS FOR JUICING

While you may not be ready for a medically supervised juice fast, you can experience health benefits from freshly juiced fruits and vegetables. And it's one way to help make sure you get a minimum of five servings of fruits and vegetables in your diet each day. On an ongoing basis, I drink a glass of fresh juice daily.

• To make lemon water, use the juice of one lemon per glass of water. You may add honey to taste if sweeteners have not been restricted from your diet.

• The vegetable juice amounts are approximate, not measured or juiced separately. The fruit juice may be replaced with another vegetable juice. I do not, nor do I recommend, mixing fruits and vegetables in the same juice. It causes gas and stomach upset. Wait 30 minutes from your last sip of one type of juice before drinking another type.

• I peel my carrots prior to juicing, but not my fruit, unless it's something like pineapple or kiwi. I always use a fine strainer to remove any pulp after juicing too.

• Unless you have a twin-gear extruder type juicer that crushes the food instead of spinning and shredding, you need to drink the juice immediately after juicing. The nutrients won't survive a refrigerator stay. Juice and drink. The twin-gear type can be refrigerated for up to 48 hours.

• If you feel guilty about throwing away the pulp, start a compost pile. The fiber can also be mixed into dog food, or you could make an occasional carrot cake.

RETRAIN YOUR TASTE BUDS

It breaks my heart to hear that one of my Crohn's acquaintances gives her baby a bottle of chocolate milk every morning followed by little doughnuts, soda pop, brownies, candy and more chocolate milk throughout the day. Her family is grouchy and irritable and always screaming at each other. Is it any wonder, when you look at the food some adults and children put in their mouths? Even Ensure, a product often given to Crohn's and colitis patients at the hospital, lists corn syrup solids as one of the main ingredients.

We need to educate ourselves on nutrition, and not wait for television commercials to tell us what to eat. The first Crohn's diet given to me was "eat nothing raw, nothing fresh, very bland, no fiber, the whiter the better, white bread, white rice...." It's sad, and people are dying needlessly. Don't be one of them. Your taste buds *can* be retrained to enjoy foods that are good for you.

Always take two bites of something new. Don't turn up your nose after one bite; it takes two bites to retrain! Think about it. It really works.

In Closing

I would like to thank each of you for your interest in Taste of Health Ministries. I hope that the recipes will be pleasing to your taste buds as well as your bodies. Please continue to remember my ministry in your prayers, as I will you. I will be praying for your speedy healing. God gave each one of our bodies the ability to heal itself. We don't have to wait for a miracle and hope He'll pick us next to be healed. All of our dietary needs are laid out in the original diet given to Adam and Eve (Genesis 1:29-30). Remember one thing above all else: *Raw food is cell food!* If you own a juicer, you may want to blow the dust off and begin using it.

Please be advised: When you start to drink fresh juices and eat a more healthful diet or go on a parasite cleanse you start to detox! This can bring on headaches, usually starting the second day of drinking fresh juices. You may have a caffeine-withdrawal headache. You may feel flu-like symptoms. You may experience diarrhea with mucus. Just know it is all part of your body starting to clean house, and the headaches do go away about the fourth day. It gets better, but if you don't expect it, it can fool you into thinking that eating good food is bad for you. You will feel more energy as the detox subsides. Detox symptoms that persist beyond a few days need to be investigated by a doctor.

As you struggle with your health challenges, pray for the answers. God will lead you to them!

I began this ministry because I have a burning passion to help sick people get better. I have learned that in all my giving to you, I am the one who is blessed. You can never outgive the Lord!

God bless you in your endeavors towards health,
Your friend in Christ,

Barbara Kerr

Barbara Kerr

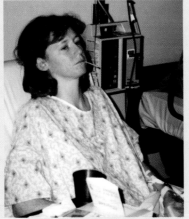

One day after ileostomy surgery, October 1994, I felt as though I had been defeated and that I would never be able to help anyone.

As you struggle with your health challenges, pray for the answers. God will lead you to them!

Two weeks after ileostomy surgery, I knew I had made the right decision. An ileostomy isn't the end of the world! It gave me a second chance at life and allowed me to continue my commitment to take better care of my body and help others learn about the importance of a good diet.

ADDITIONAL RESOURCES

QUESTIONS?

If you are willing to pay for the phone call, I will gladly answer any questions I can. My phone hours are noon to 2 p.m. (E.S.T.) only, and phone appointments are limited to 20 minutes. Thank you for your cooperation. You may reach me at (803) 936-1714. My fax number is (803) 936-9161. If you have any difficulty reaching me, you can contact Three Angels Broadcasting Network at 1-800-752-3226. They will have a current listing.

BIBLIOGRAPHY

Here are a few of my favorite health books. I don't necessarily endorse or believe every single thing each author writes. I use my common sense and measure what they have to say against my gut feeling, personal experience, the Bible and other writers. I hope you will be able to find them helpful as well.

Balch, Phyllis A., C.N.C., and James F. Balch, M. D. *RX Prescription for Cooking and Dietary Wellness*. Greenfield, Ind.: P.A.B. Publishing, Inc., 1993.

Batmanghelidj, F. , M.D. *Your Body's Many Cries for Water*. Falls Church, Va.: Global Health Solutions, Inc., 1992.

Carter, Albert E. *The Miracles Of Rebound Exercise*. Snohomish, Wash.: Snohomish Printing Co., 1979.

Diamond, Harvey and Marilyn. *Fit for Life*. New York, N.Y.: Warner Books, 1985.

Gage, Diane. *Aloe Vera*. Rochester, Vt.: Healing Arts Press, 1988.

Malkmus, George H., Ph.D. *God's Way to Ultimate Health*. New Canaan, Conn.: Keats Publishing, 1994.

Mindell, Earl, R.Ph., Ph.D. *Garlic, the Miracle Nutrient*. Brushton, N.Y.: Teach Services, 1983.

Walker, Dr. Norman W. *Fresh Vegetables and Fruit Juices*. Prescott, Ariz.: Norwalk Press, 1978.

DISTRIBUTORS

Awareness Corporation carries Clear, the parasite killer I mention in the afterword (page 120), and Experience, to help regulate bowels. Call 1-800-692-9273 to become a V.I.P. customer. You can use the ID number 4935301.

Better Than Milk, a division of Fuller Life, Inc., makes a product called Better Than Ice Creme. It is a soy, nondairy powdered ice cream mix that tastes fantastic. It can be purchased at a health food store, or call 1-800-227-2320.

Country Life Natural Foods offers a complete line of reasonably priced natural, whole and organic foods to enable you to enjoy the recipes in this cookbook.

They carry some of the featured ingredients such as Emes kosher gelatin, pure maple syrup, Bragg's liquid aminos, McKay's chicken-style seasoning, Mori-Nu tofu, whole grains including quinoa and whole-wheat pastry flour, and a complete line of herbs and spices.

Over 1,200 items are available and can be shipped directly to your door via UPS or, for larger orders, by their own delivery trucks.

To order a free catalog, contact Country Life Natural Foods, P.O. Box 489, Pullman, MI 49450, 1-800-456-7694, *www.clnf.org*, sales@clnf.org

Follow Your Heart of Canoga Park, Calif., carries Vegenaise. Call (818) 347-9946, or look for it at your health food store.

Hallelujah Acres can help you order barley green, which I discuss in my letter (page 120). Write to P.O. Box 2388, Shelby, NC 28151 or call (704) 481-1700, fax (704) 481-0345. Also ask for their free copy of *Back to the Garden* newsletter. It's great!

Harvest-Time Foods & Bakery carries sprouted wheat bread, featured on page 95. To order the bread or any of the ingredients, write Susan Grimm at 3719 Main St., Thompsonville, IL 62890, phone: (618) 627-4444, fax: (618) 627-2114, susan326@juno.com.

Metagenics, based in San Clemente, Calif., carries Ultra Dophilus DF (mentioned in the afterword, page 120). Call their corporate office, (949) 366-0818, to find a doctor distributor in your area.

Mosaicwares provided many of the serving pieces for my food photos: the epergne on page 19, the stand on page 31, the tray on page 37 and the cake stand on page 75. You can reach them at Mosaicwares, 160 Tycos Drive, Toronto, Ontario, M6B 1W8, phone: (416) 787-5526, fax: (416) 787-5424, *www.mosaicwares.com*, mosaic@gncom.com.

Mrs. Mango & Co. distributes delicious hibiscus tea. Write or call: 3500 U.S. Highway 1 S., Rockledge, FL 32955, (407) 631-1194.

NEWSTART can give you more information about God's laws for health. Contact the Weimar Institute NEWSTART® Lifestyle Center at (530) 637-4111 or P.O. Box 486, Weimar, CA 95736. The NEWSTART acronym, page 131, is used by permission.

Nutri-Line Foods makes Bill's Best products, including Chik Nish chicken-style seasoning. Call (530) 876-0823 to find a local distributor or to request recipes.

HEALTHFUL LIVING AND THE BIBLE

For a free study guide on what the Bible has to say about healthful living, write to: Health for Life Bible Study Guide, P.O. Box 2034, Lexington, SC, 29071-2034. Please be sure to mention this cookbook when you write.

JUICING CLINIC

For information on the healthy lifestyle juicing clinic Barbara Kerr attended, call (407) 645-3626. Ask for Doctor Sung Min Im.

THREE ANGELS BROADCASTING NETWORK (3ABN)

P.O. Box 220
West Frankfort, IL 62896
Phone: (618) 627-4651
Fax: (618) 627-2726
E-mail: mail@3abn.org
Internet: *www.3abn.org*

HOW TO VIEW 3ABN:

Besides the 108 North American rebroadcast stations, there are several other ways you can tune in to 3ABN:

Dominion Sky Angel

Sky Angel's digital system carries many Christian channels, including 3ABN on channel 9710. Call 3ABN for information on dish systems and subscriptions.

GE-4 satellite at 101° West

Watch 3ABN on a subscription-free digital dish system. If you already have a compatible dish system, you can tune in with these parameters:

Frequency: 11.807 MHz; Symbol rate: 4.000.000 ms/s; F.E.C.: 3/4; Polarization: Horizontal. Call 3ABN for equipment specifications or to purchase a system.

World Wide Web

Visit *www.3abn.org*. You can see 3ABN Television or listen to 3ABN Radio online 24 hours a day. Also view additional schedule information, read the latest 3ABN news and more.

ACKNOWLEDGMENTS

Claudia

Dr. Berkelhammer

Mom

Bill

Nathan

Sandi

Donna

Linda (and Fluffy)

I would like to thank my best friend and funniest woman in the world, Claudia Welty, for saving my life and befriending me when I was a sick chick. Without her endless phone calls, care packages, cards, support, wisdom, prayers, friendship and laughter, this book would not have become a reality. Thank you.

I would like to thank my doctor and gastroenterologist, Charles Berkelhammer, M.D., for not only writing the foreword for this book, but for being the most compassionate, caring physician I have ever had the privilege of knowing. The extreme dedication he shows to his patients can never be measured and I publicly thank him for saving my life!

I would like to thank my mother, JoAnn Hall, for teaching me how to cook and for instilling a passion to experiment in the kitchen. I would also like to thank her for all the months she took care of me and my infant son, Nathan, when I was in and out of hospitals.

I would like to thank my husband, Bill, and son, Nathan, for the many experimental meals they have endured over the last four years, and their patience during the days spent away from home travelling.

I would like to thank my sister Sandi Brewer and my neighbor Donna Vaughn for being my taste testers and for always being honest.

I would like to thank Three Angels Broadcasting Network for their support, love, and endless invitations to tape cooking programs; and Linda Shelton, who is as funny, sweet and kind "off-camera" as she is "on air."

I would like to thank Roberta Jupp, R.D., for her dietary expertise and for volunteering many hours to formulate the nutritional data for this project.

I would like to thank Lea Hardy for her editing talents and patience
even when the computer kept crashing and losing her work.

I would like to thank Judy Anderson for her beautiful design and color choices, and
Jan Asher Dolph for layout and editing. They met an impossible deadline and
volunteered many hours in a labor of love. And thanks to the many people at Coffey
Communications (especially Joa and Don) who helped them support my project.

I would like to thank Pat Crawford for the excellent photographs in this book,
for secretly tasting the food during the photo shoot—and loving it, and for all
the little "extras" he donated to this project. You're awesome, Pat!

I would like to thank my food stylist Chris Valanne for her beautiful
and creative food presentation, but most of all for her wacky
sense of humor that kept the tense moments light.

I would like to thank my food stylist Fran Woosley for her
artistic talents and her calm, steady work under pressure.

I would like to thank all those who have written letters of encouragement
thanking me for this cooking ministry and everyone who has prayed for me,
phoned and sent e-mail. Your enthusiasm is contagious!

I would like to thank above all the Almighty God, who answered my many prayers for
healing by teaching me His natural laws of health and healing: Nutrition, Exercise,
pure Water, Sunshine, Temperance, fresh Air, proper Rest and Trust in God. He wants
us to know in this age of chronic diseases that we don't have to be sick! We can enjoy
abundant health, joy and peace when we follow God's plan for our bodies. He will
give you the **NEW START** you're looking for. Won't you ask Him today?

Roberta

Lea

Judy

Jan

Pat

Chris

Fran

131 Acknowledgments

INDEX

Boldface numbers refer to a photo of the prepared recipe.

INDEX

Boldface numbers refer to a photo of the prepared recipe.

CUPS

U.S. cups	Metric
¼ cup	60 ml
⅓ cup	70 ml
½ cup	120 ml
⅔ cup	150 ml
¾ cup	180 ml
1 cup	240 ml
1½ cups	360 ml
2 cups	480 ml
3 cups	720 ml
4 cups	960 ml

OVEN TEMPERATURES

Fahrenheit	Celsius	Gas	Description
225°F	110°C	¼	Cool
250°F	120°C	½	Cool
275°F	140°C	1	Very low
300°F	150°C	2	Very low
325°F	160°C	3	Low
325°F	170°C	3	Moderate
350°F	180°C	4	Moderate
375°F	190°C	5	Moderately hot
400°F	200°C	6	Hot
425°F	220°C	7	Hot
450°F	230°C	8	Very hot

SPOONS

Imperial	Metric
¼ tsp	1.25 ml
½ tsp	2.5 ml
1 tsp	5 ml
2 tsp	10 ml
3 tsp/1 tbsp	15 ml
2 tbsp	30 ml
3 tbsp	45 ml
4 tbsp	60 ml
5 tbsp	75 ml
6 tbsp	90 ml

VOLUME

Imperial	Metric	Imperial	Metric
1 fl oz	30 ml	16 fl oz	480 ml
2 fl oz	60 ml	1 pint	480 ml
4 fl oz	120 ml	2 pints	960 ml
6 fl oz	180 ml	1 quart	960 ml
8 fl oz	250 ml	3 pints	1440 ml
10 fl oz	300 ml	4 pints	1920 ml
12 fl oz	360 ml	2 quarts	1920 ml
14 fl oz	420 ml	1 gallon	3840 m.

DIMENSIONS

Imperial	Metric	Imperial	Metric	Imperial	Metric
¹⁄₁₆ inch	2 mm	3 inches	7.5 cm	7½ inches	19 cm
⅛ inch	3 mm	3¼ inches	8 cm	8 inches	20 cm
¼ inch	5 mm	3½ inches	9 cm	8½ inches	22 cm
⅜ inch	8 mm	3¾ inches	9.5 cm	9 inches	23 cm
½ inch	10 mm/1 cm	4 inches	10 cm	9½ inches	24 cm
⅝ inch	1.5 cm	4¼ inches	11 cm	10 inches	25 cm
¾ inch	2 cm	4½ inches	12 cm	10½ inches	26 cm
1 inch	2.5 cm	4¾ inches	12.5 cm	10¾ inches	27 cm
1¼ inches	3 cm	5 inches	13 cm	11 inches	28 cm
1½ inches	4 cm	5½ inches	14 cm	11½ inches	29 cm
1¾ inches	4.5 cm	6 inches	15 cm	12 inches	30 cm
2 inches	5 cm	6¼ inches	16 cm	12½ inches	31 cm
2¼ inches	5.5 cm	6½ inches	17 cm	13 inches	33 cm
2½ inches	6 cm	7 inches	18 cm	13½ inches	34 cm
2¾ inches	7 cm				

WEIGHTS

Imperial	Metric	Imperial	Metric	Imperial	Metric
⅛ oz	5 g	4 oz	115 g	13 oz	375 g
¼ oz	10 g	4½ oz	125 g	14 oz	400 g
½ oz	15 g	5 oz	140 g	15 oz	425 g
¾ oz	20 g	5½ oz	150 g	1 lb	450 g
1 oz	25 g	6 oz	175 g	1 lb, 2 oz	500 g
1¼ oz	35 g	7 oz	200 g	1 lb, 4 oz	550 g
1½ oz	40 g	8 oz	225 g	1 lb, 5 oz	600 g
1¾ oz	50 g	9 oz	250 g	1 lb, 7 oz	650 g
2 oz	55 g	9¾ oz	275 g	1 lb, 9 oz	700 g
2¼ oz	60 g	10 oz	280 g	1 lb, 10 oz	750 g
2½ oz	70 g	10½ oz	300 g	1 lb, 12 oz	800 g
2¾ oz	75 g	11 oz	315 g	1 lb, 14 oz	850 g
3 oz	85 g	11½ oz	325 g	2 lbs	900 g
3¼ oz	90 g	12 oz	350 g	2 lbs, 2 oz	950 g
3½ oz	100 g				

ORDERING INFORMATION

COOKBOOK

Barbara Kerr's Taste of Health: A Vegetarian Crohn's & Colitis Cookbook $18.95
ISBN 1-930984-00-6

Cookbook and Video Set: *Taste of Health* and 17 cooking and health information videos
(includes 14 "3ABN Presents" specials, 12 "Food for Thought" episodes,
and 2-hour "3ABN Live") Available January 2001 .... 169.95
ISBN 1-930984-19-7

VIDEOS, AVAILABLE JANUARY 2001

All videos originally produced by Three Angels Broadcasting Network, and were aired as
"3ABN Presents" or "Food For Thought" specials.

Let's Have a Party! New Year's Eve or Super Bowl Sunday Menu (60 min.) 9.95
ISBN 1-930984-01-4

Hors d'Oeuvres (60 min.) 9.95
ISBN 1-930984-02-2

Valentine's Menu (60 min.) 9.95
ISBN 1-930984-03-0

Easter Menu (60 min.) 9.95
ISBN 1-930984-04-9

For Mother With Love (60 min.) 9.95
ISBN 1-930984-05-7

A-Camping We Will Go (60 min.) 9.95
ISBN 1-930984-06-5

Here's To Dad (60 min.) 9.95
ISBN 1-930984-07-3

Fourth of July (60 min.) 9.95
ISBN 1-930984-08-1

Happy Birthday, Baby! (60 min.) 9.95
ISBN 1-930984-09-X

Sumptuous Summer Soups (60 min.) 9.95
ISBN 1-930984-10-3

Bread Delicacies (60 min.) 9.95
ISBN 1-930984-11-1

Garden Harvest (60 min.) 9.95
ISBN 1-930984-12-X

Thanksgiving (60 min.) 9.95
ISBN 1-930984-13-8

Home for the Holidays (60 min.) 9.95
ISBN 1-930984-14-6

Food For Thought Programs One through Six (approx. 3 hours) 12.95
ISBN 1-930984-15-4

> *Summer Desserts (28 min.), Cooking with Carob (28 min.), How to Get Your Kids Off of Sugar (28 min.),
> Sugarless Desserts (28 min.), Healthy Drinks (28 min.), Sandwiches (28 min.)*

Food For Thought Programs Seven through Twelve (approx. 3 hours) 12.95
ISBN 1-930984-16-2

> *A Romanian Meal (28 min.), Cooking with Carrots (28 min.), Cooking with Garlic (28 min.), Cooking with Oats
> (28 min.), Quinoa–Supergrain of the Future (28 min.), Juice Your Way to Health (28 min.)*

"3ABN Live" with Doctor Sung Min Im and Barbara Kerr (120 min.) 12.95
ISBN 1-930984-17-0

> *Video deals with cancer, water testing, making vegetable juice and Crohn's control; includes
> three salad dressing recipes.*

Six Inspirational Duets featuring Barbara Kerr and her sister, Sandi Brewer 14.95
ISBN 1-930984-18-9

*Current prices
and information
can be found on
my Web site at
www.tasteofhealth.net.*

JUICE MACHINES

Shipping charges are $9 for each juicer ordered. Money orders, payable to Taste of Health Ministries, or credit cards only. Visit my Web site, *www.tasteofhealth.net*, to see pictures.

L'Equip Juicer . . . . (Retail: $250) My price: $199
• *Less foam, more taste, more nutrition*
• *Twelve-year warranty; UL-approved; continuous juicing; large feeder tube; high-quality stainless steel bowl;
blade basket; innovative bag holder; computer-controlled motor; rated voltage: 120V 60hz; horse power: 3/4; current:
5A; lowest RPMs of any pulp-ejection juicer*

Champion Household Juicer . . . . (Retail: $271) My price: $215
• *Hardened steel shaft; 1/3 horse power GE motor; 100% nylon and stainless steel components.*
• *Warranty: 1-year motor, 5-year parts*
• *Specify white or almond color*

Green Power Juicer . . . . (Retail: $599) My price: $495
• *Prolonged juice storage time (48 hours)*
• *Juices wheat grass and leafy greens*
• *Includes fine/coarse screen, juice pitcher, cleaning brush, plunger and strainer; rice cake and pasta attachment
standard*
• *Twin-gear triturating action with low speed; 110 RPM*

TO ORDER

Call or write: Taste of Health Ministries, P.O. Box 38, Gaston, SC 29053
Telephone: (803) 936-1714; Fax: (803) 936-9161

Ordering by mail: Please print all addresses clearly, and include a daytime telephone number.

Ordering by phone: If leaving a phone message, be sure to speak slowly and clearly, and spell unusual names or words.

Credit card orders: I am now accepting Visa and MasterCard; your order must include the card number, expiration date and your signature.

Shipping charges: $4.50 for all orders under $45. For orders over $45, add 10% for shipping and handling. Add additional $4.50 shipping and handling for each cookbook shipped to an additional address. Please call for shipping rates outside the continental U.S. (For juicers, see above.)

Sales tax: South Carolina residents, please add 5% sales tax to entire order.